GCSE Maths by RSL

Non-Calculator, Higher Level

This book contains six realistic GCSE Mathematics papers, modelled on the non-calculator exams set by all boards for the 9-1 syllabus. Three papers are worth 80 marks and three 100. They cover all the most common non-calculator question types at this level.

The papers are accompanied by highly detailed, *teaching* solution pages. Studied carefully, these offer a thorough foundation for an excellent performance at GCSE. Every solution is explained step-by-step, in the same way that I show these techniques to my students. Hand-written answers demonstrate the sort of working which is effective in exams, often with several alternatives. Core knowledge is highlighted along the way.

The mark schemes in this book are designed for ease of use, so that they will make sense to people who do not have experience of marking. They have been structured so that the outcome will be the same as (or very close to) that which would be given by a formal mark scheme.

How to use these materials

It is best to complete these papers in order. Although each test and mark sheet can stand alone, used in sequence they will build up your skills steadily. Frequent cross-references will direct you to places earlier in the book where methods are explained more fully, in the event that you need to revise them.

When you are correcting your work, it is a good idea to take notes of any important points: this will help you to remember them. If an answer could be improved, it is often worth repeating it with reference to the examples. Where alternative methods are suggested, it can be useful to try them for yourself.

These papers can be used with or without time limits. **The most important thing is to study the solution pages slowly and thoroughly.** If marking is rushed, important lessons will be missed. When the main skills have been acquired, it is usually a fairly simple matter to speed up your work using exam boards' past papers. Timing problems are almost always caused by a lack of confidence with core techniques.

A note on marking

<u>Follow-through marking</u>: Where this applies, it is indicated in the mark schemes by the abbreviation "F.T.". For example, if part **(b)** of a question depends on the answer to part **(a)**, and part **(a)** was answered incorrectly, the same mistake should not be penalised twice. **(b)** should be marked as though the values taken from **(a)** are correct.

The mark schemes make reference to "major" and "minor" errors. This comes down to judgement, but broadly speaking a minor error is a slip in concentration (writing 2.02 as 2.002, for example), whereas a major error is something more fundamental, such as using an inappropriate technique.

We are a family business in a competitive marketplace. We are constantly improving and expanding our range, in order to publish ever-better resources for our customers – in particular, families who find that our books offer better value than expensive private tuition.

If you have any feedback or questions, please let us know! You can get in touch through our website at **www.rsleducational.co.uk**, where you can also view our up-to-date range of publications, or by emailing **robert@rsleducational.co.uk**.

If you like this book, please tell your friends and write a review on Amazon!

Also available

- ➢ GCSE German by RSL: Volumes 1 and 2
- ➢ GCSE Spanish by RSL: Volumes 1 and 2
- ➢ GCSE French by RSL: Volumes 1 and 2
- ➢ RSL 11+ Comprehension: Volumes 1 and 2
- ➢ RSL 11+ Maths
- ➢ RSL 8+ Comprehension
- ➢ RSL 13+ Comprehension
- ➢ *11 Plus Lifeline* (printable comprehension, maths, reasoning and creative writing material): **www.11pluslifeline.com**

GCSE Maths by RSL (Non-Calculator, Higher Level) by Robert Lomax
Published by RSL Educational
Copyright © Robert Lomax 2016

I am grateful to James Rogers for his wise advice and invaluable corrections. Any errors or omissions are mine.

Contents

Paper 1 (80 marks)

If you wish to complete this paper in timed conditions, allow 1hr 30mins.

1   Work out 9.85×5.2

.... [2]

2   It takes 3 cats 4 weeks to catch 12 mice. The cats are four years old.

Assume that:

- All four-year-old cats catch mice at the same, steady rate, and this is not affected by the time of year.
- The cats do not work as a team.

(a)   How long would it take the 3 cats to catch 18 mice?

.... [2]

(b)   How many mice would 2 of the cats catch in 12 weeks?

.... [2]

(c)   3 cats catch 12 mice in 4 weeks.

Brianna calculates that, if one of the cats lives for 15 years, it is likely to catch 780 mice in its lifetime, because $1 \times 52 \times 15 = 780$

What extra assumption has Brianna made?

How has this assumption affected the magnitude of her answer? Explain your reasoning.

[3]

3   ABCD is a rectangle.

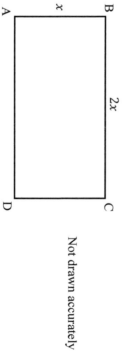

Not drawn accurately

(a)   Find the length BD, giving your answer in terms of x.

.... [2]

(b) The area of the rectangle is 50m².

Find the value of x.

.... [2]

4 Find the meeting point of the lines $2y = x - 10$ and $y = 13 - 4x$.

.... [3]

5 N is a negative number.

What is the value of N multiplied by the negative reciprocal of N?

.... [2]

6 The plan, front elevation and side elevation of a solid shape are drawn on a cm grid.

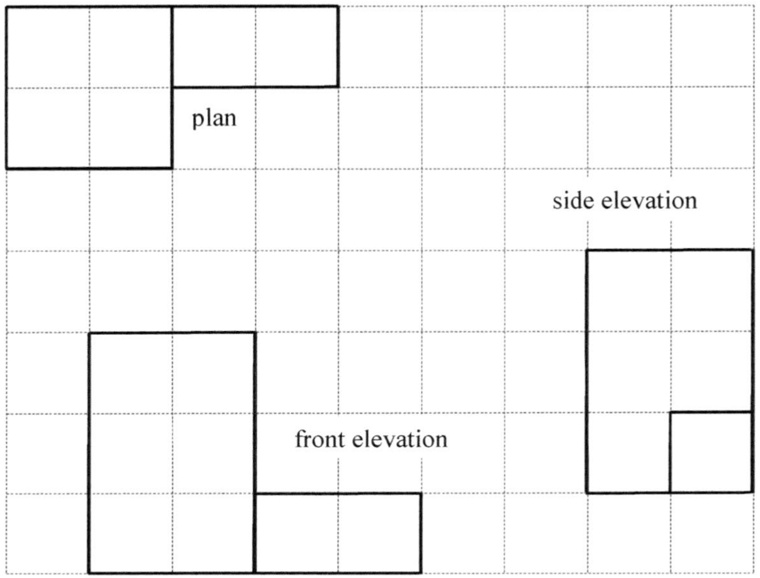

Calculate the volume of the shape in cm³.

.... [3]

7   The Airbus A380 aircraft can fly 16,000km without refuelling, rounded
    to the nearest 1,000km.

    Find the greatest and smallest possible values for **R**, the number of times
    the aircraft would need to be filled with fuel if it flew a total distance of
    742,500km exactly.

    Then complete the error interval.

    Assume that the aircraft always flies the maximum possible distance on
    each flight.

    .... ≤ **R** ≤ .... **[4]**

8   The amount of money held in savings by 21 randomly selected people is
    shown in the following scatter graph, plotted against their ages.

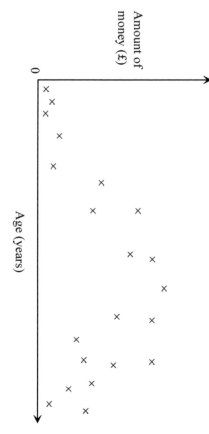

Amount of
money (£)

0   Age (years)

    (a)   (i)   Describe in your own words the <u>relationship</u> between
                 people's ages and the value of their savings.

                                                                        [2]

          (ii)   Suggest a reason for this relationship.

                                                                        [1]

(b) What kind of <u>correlation</u>, if any, is there between people's ages and the value of their savings?

Circle the correct answer.

[1]

positive correlation   negative correlation   no correlation

9   Solve $3x - 5 \leq -\frac{3}{2} + 2x$

.... [2]

10   (a)   Evaluate each of the following, giving your answer as a rational number or in surd form.

(i) $\dfrac{\sqrt{324}}{\sqrt{72}}$

.... [2]

(ii) $7(\overline{\sqrt{7}})^{-3}$

.... [2]

(iii) -26^0

.... [1]

(b)   Express 2×9^{-1} as a recurring decimal.

11   ABC and ADE are triangles.

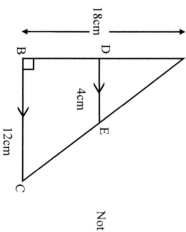

Not drawn accurately

What fraction of triangle ABC is occupied by triangle ADE?

.... **[4]**

12   My bath has two taps.

The hot tap emits water at a rate of 10 litres per minute.

The cold tap emits water at a rate of 16 litres per minute.

I run the hot tap for 9 minutes, then I run the cold tap for 4 minutes, then I run both taps for 2 minutes and 30 seconds.

(a)   Draw a rate-time graph, showing the overall rate of water flowing into my bath.

Assume that I can turn the taps off or on instantaneously and that they only run at full rate when on.

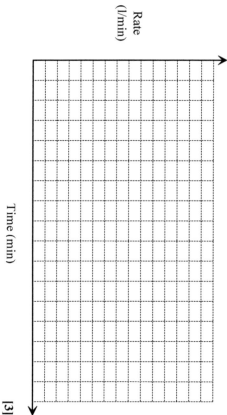

Rate
(l/min)

Time (min)

[3]

(b)   Work out the total volume of water in my bath when I have finished running it.

.... **[3]**

14 I weigh the chocolate bars in my cupboard. All are between 30g and 90g.

This table shows the probability that the mass m of a randomly selected chocolate bar lies in a certain range.

Mass m g	Probability
$30 \leq m < 40$	0.1
$40 \leq m < 50$	0.325
$50 \leq m < 60$	$2x$
$60 \leq m < 70$	x
$70 \leq m < 80$	0.1
$80 \leq m < 90$	0.025

(a) Find the value of x.

.... **[2]**

(b) Find the probability that a randomly chosen chocolate bar weighs less than 60g.

.... **[2]**

(c) 13 of the chocolate bars each weigh between 40g and 50g.

How many chocolate bars are in my cupboard?

.... **[2]**

---

13 (a) Completely factorise

$20x^2y^2 - 4y^3$

.... **[2]**

(b) Expand and simplify

$(2y - 3)(y - 5)$

.... **[2]**

(c) Solve by factorising

$2x^2 + 4x = 70$

.... **[3]**

15 $f(x) = 5 - 3x$

$fg(x) = 7$

Find $g(x)$

.... [2]

16 Solid **T** and solid **V** are mathematically similar.

The surface areas of **T** and **V** are in the ratio $9 : 25$

The mass of solid **T** is 540kg.

Show that the mass of solid **V** is 2500kg.

.... [4]

17 XYZ is a triangle.

R and **T** are the midpoints of XY and ZY respectively.

a, **b** and **c** are vectors.

Not drawn accurately

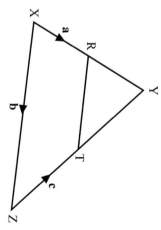

$\overrightarrow{XR} = \mathbf{a}, \overrightarrow{XZ} = \mathbf{b}, \overrightarrow{ZT} = \mathbf{c}$

(a)   Write the following in terms of **a**, **b** and **c** (you are not required to use all of the vectors in each answer).

(i) $\overrightarrow{XT}$

.... [1]

(ii) $\overrightarrow{ZR}$

.... [1]

(b)   Show that $\overrightarrow{RT}$ is parallel to and half the length of $\overrightarrow{XZ}$.

.... [3]

18   The diagram shows a circle, centre (0 , 0).

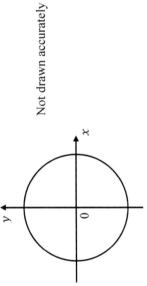

Not drawn accurately

The area of the circle is 16π.

(a)   Find the equation of the circle.

.... **[3]**

(b)   Another circle has centre (3 , −2).

Find the equation of the line which is a tangent to this circle at the
point (6 , 2).

Write your answer in the form $ay = bx + c$ where a, b and c are
integers.

Paper 1 – Solutions

1

$$9.85 \times 5.2$$

$$\begin{array}{r} 9.85 \\ \times \ 5.2 \\ \hline 1.9.7.0 \\ 4.9.2.5.0 \\ \hline 5.1.2.2.0 \end{array}$$

] 3 digits after decimal points

(Extra 0)

$$51.220$$

$$51.220 = 51.22$$

This is a fairly simple warm-up question ... but it is amazing how many people forget their paper arithmetic techniques.

Here are some tips for multiplication, in case you are one of those people with a shaky memory:

- Put the shorter (not necessarily smaller) number on the second row.

- Don't forget to add a 0 at the *right hand end of the second row of your working* (between the horizontal lines) – and two 0s on the next row, and so on.

- Remember that you place the decimal point by adding up *the total number of digits after decimal points* **in the question** (above the first horizontal line), then *counting back this many places from the right hand end of the answer (including zeros)*.

Remember to remove any unnecessary 0s before giving your final answer. 51.220 might lose you a mark.

Marking: 1 mark for correct method with a minor error. 0 marks if contains a significant error. **[2 marks]**

2 (a)

Cats	Weeks	Mice
3	4 $\div 4$ 1 $\times 6$ 6	12 $\div 4$ 3 $\times 6$ 18

$\therefore$ 3

∴ 3

6 weeks

It is enormously helpful to organise questions of this sort (where you must adjust proportions) in a table.

∴ ∴ means 'therefore'. You will see this symbol frequently in these solution pages.

- If it takes 3 cats 4 weeks to catch 12 mice, then they must catch 3 mice per week (assuming, as the question states, that they catch mice at a mercilessly consistent rate): the number of weeks and the number of mice is directly proportional.

- 18 mice is 6 lots of 3, so it must also take them 6 times as long.

- Therefore the answer is 6 weeks.

You could take this more direct approach:

Cats	Weeks	Mice
3	4 $\times 1.5$ 6	12 $\times 1.5$ 18

∴ 3

6 weeks

You could also solve the problem by reducing further:

- If 3 cats catch 3 mice per week (from the first solution), then **1 cat catches 1 mouse per week** ... and so on.

Don't forget to write 'weeks': you risk losing a mark if you don't give the correct unit of time.

3 (a)

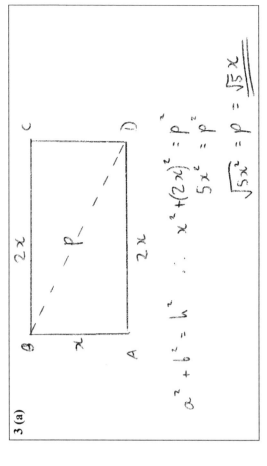

$$a^2 + b^2 = h^2 \quad \therefore \quad x^2 + (2x)^2 = p^2$$
$$5x^2 = p^2$$
$$\sqrt{5x^2} = p = \sqrt{5}\,x$$

It is enormously useful to sketch and label, when faced with a geometric problem.

This question is based around Pythagoras' Theorem, which allows you to calculate the length of the *hypotenuse* (the longest side) of a right-angled triangle:

- *The square of the hypotenuse equals the sum of the squares of the other two sides.*
- Or $a^2 + b^2 = h^2$
- ... Or $a^2 + b^2 = c^2$, as some people learn it.

For convenience, I use the letter p in my working to represent the distance BD.

The starting point is to notice that if BC is $2x$ long, then (because of the properties of a rectangle) AD must be the same length.

From this point, it is a matter of simple algebra.

- **Remember that $(2x)^2 = 4x^2$, not $2x^2$.**
- You are likely to lose a mark if you leave your answer in the form $\sqrt{5x^2}$, rather than simplifying to $\sqrt{5}x$.

Marking: 1 mark for a decent attempt at Pythagoras' Theorem. **[2 marks]**

Marking: 1 mark if a minor error. **[2 marks]**

(b)

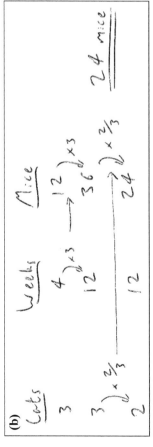

You could follow more than one route here. The example works by adjusting the time, then the number of mice:

- In 12 weeks, the cats will catch 3 times as many mice as in 4 weeks.
- If there are 2 rather than 3 cats, this will reduce the number of mice caught by $\frac{1}{3}$ (therefore $\times \frac{2}{3}$).
- Therefore they catch 24 mice.

Marking: 1 mark for a minor error. **[2 marks]**

(c) *She has assumed that a cat catches mice at the same rate throughout its life. This has probably made her answer too high, because a kitten or an elderly cat would be unlikely to catch as many mice as a four-year-old.*

You need to clearly answer all three parts of the question:

- *What was* Brianna's assumption?
- *How will* this have affected Brianna's answer?
- *Why will* the assumption have had this effect?

Be careful not to simply re-state the information given at the beginning of the question: that the cats catch mice at the same, steady rate. This applied to the four-year-old cats. You need to make clear how Brianna's extra assumption, that this work rate continues throughout a cat's life, is different.

Marking: 1 mark for each bullet-point above. A significantly different answer must be reasonable and well justified if it is to receive marks. **[3 marks]**

(b)

$$2x \times x = 50$$
$$2x^2 = 50$$
$$x^2 = 25$$
$$x = \sqrt{25} = 5$$

$$\underline{\underline{5\,m}}$$

This is likely to be simpler than part **(a)**.

Although you probably don't need reminding, the area of a rectangle is *length* × *width*.

Don't forget to give the correct units (metres)!

Marking: 1 mark for correct method with an error. 1 mark if answer correct but incorrect units or none. **[2 marks]**

4   The basic principle here is that *two lines meet where the values of x and y are the same in both their equations* – in other words, where they share a point (x, y).

• Because of this, you need to *solve the equations simultaneously*, finding the values of x and y which work for both of them.

There are many ways to do this, but here are three sensible approaches.

• I have left out the option of graphing (drawing graphs of the equations and finding where they meet): this works well where the solutions happen to be integers (whole numbers), but can lead to inaccuracy otherwise, so I do not recommend it.

Method 1

Ⓐ $\begin{pmatrix} 2y = x - 10 \\ y = 13 - 4x \end{pmatrix}$ $\;[×2] \; ∴ \; ⓑ\;2y = 26 - 8x$

Since $2y = 2y$, right-hand side of Ⓐ = right-hand side of Ⓑ.

∴ $x - 10 = 26 - 8x$
$9x - 10 = 26$
$9x = 36$
$x = \dfrac{36}{9} = 4$

Substitute into Ⓐ:

$2y = x - 10$
∴ $2y = 4 - 10 = -6$
$y = \dfrac{-6}{2} = -3$

$\underline{\underline{(4, -3)}}$

This method begins by making each equation equal to $2y$.

This allows you to combine the equations, eliminating the y completely: because the lines meet at a single point, $2y$ must represent the same number in both equations.

• When you solve simultaneous equations, you always look to eliminate (get rid of) one letter at a time.

Once you know what x is, take a '$y =$' (or '$2y =$') equation from the beginning of your working, and insert your solution for x.

• Solve this to find y.

Method 2

$$\left(2y = x - 10 \quad \therefore \quad y = \frac{x}{2} - 5\right)$$

$$y = 13 - 4x$$

$$\therefore \quad 13 - 4x = \frac{x}{2} - 5$$

$$(8) \quad -4x = \frac{x}{2} - 5$$

$$18 = \frac{9x}{2}$$

$$36 = 9x$$

$$\frac{36}{9} = 4 = x$$

$$\left(y = \frac{x}{2} - 5\right) \quad \therefore \quad y = \frac{4}{2} - 5 = 2 - 5 = -3$$

$$x = 4 \qquad\qquad (4, -3)$$

Method 2 uses the same approach as **Method 1**, except that, instead of multiplying the second equation by 2 to make '$2y =$', it halves the first equation to make '$y =$'.

Method 3

$$\left(y = 13 - 4x \quad \therefore \quad 2y = 26 - 8x\right)$$

$$2y = x - 10$$

$$(A) : 2y = 26 - 8x$$

$$(B) \quad 2y = -10 + x$$

$$(A) - (B) : \quad 0 = 36 - 9x$$

$$9x = 36$$

$$x = 4$$

$$\left(y = 13 - 4x\right) \quad \therefore \quad y = 13 - 16 = -3 \quad (4, -3)$$

$$x = 4$$

This method is slightly different:

- **Rearrange the equations** so that the y, x and constant (number) terms are in the same order in both of them.
- **Subtract the equations** from each other in order to remove x or y. (Sometimes you will need to add them instead, if one negative value is involved.)
- **Solve the new equation** to find the remaining variable.
- **Use this answer** to find the other variable, as explained below **Method 1**.

Marking: 1 mark for an attempt to solve simultaneously. 2 marks for correct method with minor errors. **[3 marks]**

5

The *reciprocal* of a number is $\dfrac{1}{\text{the number}}$, so the *negative reciprocal* is $-\dfrac{1}{\text{the number}}$

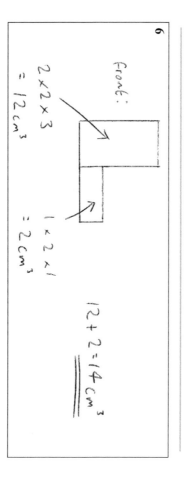

$$N \times \left(-\frac{1}{N}\right) = -\frac{N}{N} = \underline{-1}$$

You could also solve this question using the laws of indices (covered in **Question 10(a)(ii)** below):

$$N \times -N^{-1} = -N^{1-1} = -N^0 = -1$$

Any number divided by itself (except for 0) equals 1. *This is also true for negative numbers!* Don't let irrelevant information distract you: it is unimportant that **N** is negative. A positive value of **N** would give the same answer.

Marking: 1 mark if answer is 1. No marks if other errors. **[2 marks]**

6

front:

2×2×3 = 12cm³

1×2×1 = 2cm³

12+2 = 14 cm³

In the example I have drawn a sketch of the front elevation as a way of taking notes. Of course, you could save time by doing this on the diagram in the question paper.

The maths here is easy: the question is really testing whether you can imagine a 3D shape with only a set of plans to help you.
The *side elevation* isn't very useful in this question!

• You can see from the *plan view* that the solid has a left hand section which has a 2cm × 2cm base. From the *front elevation*, you can see that this section is 3cm high: 2 × 2 × 3 = 12cm³.

• The right hand section has a 2cm base and is 1cm high: 2 × 1 × 1 = 2cm³.
• Add these together, and the total volume of the solid is 14cm³.

Marking: 2 marks if correct answer with wrong units or none. 2 marks if a minor error. 1 mark for a weak attempt at a correct method **[3 marks]**

7

$$15,500 \leq \text{distance per flight} < 16,500$$

$$\frac{742,500}{15,500} = \frac{7425}{155} = \frac{1484}{31}$$

47.8...

$$\frac{742,500}{16,500} = \frac{7425}{165} = \frac{1484}{33}$$

44.9...

$$\underline{45 \leq R \leq 48}$$

This is obviously an unrealistic scenario: an aeroplane which always flies until its fuel tanks are completely empty, and always happens to find an airport at exactly the right moment! However, as a mathematician you will be familiar with questions which seem a long way from reality.

• First, you need to work out the *greatest and smallest possible distances* the aircraft might fly without refuelling. If 16,000km is correct to the nearest 1000km, the actual distance must be between 15,500km and 16,500km.

- To find the **upper bound**, you must **divide by the smaller number.**
- To find the **lower bound**, you must **divide by the larger number.**
- Then **round up** to the next integer (see explanation below).

It might initially be unclear *whether to round your answers up or down*. Think about it like this:

You are finding the number of times the aircraft must be filled with fuel; in other words, you are finding *how many loads of fuel it will get through.* If it needs 47.8 full loads of fuel, then the only way to achieve this is to fill it 48 times (just as, if it needed 0.8 tank-loads of fuel, you would have to fill it once). **Even if it needed only 47.1 loads of fuel, it would still need to be filled 48 times.** Similarly, 44.9 loads of fuel require the plane's tanks to be filled 45 times.

If your **long division** is rusty, it is worth practising! For reasons of space, I won't describe the method in full here. However, bear in mind that you can add 0s after a decimal point below the 'bus shelter' to find a more accurate answer. (Although I do it, this is not strictly necessary here: as soon as you can see that the answer is between 47 and 48, for example, you have what you need for your answer.)

Marking: 3 marks if minor errors (e.g. rounding down, or a division error which alters the answer). 2 marks for a decent attempt but significantly wrong working. 1 mark for a vaguely reasonable method with major errors. **[4 marks]**

8 (a) (i) *People tend to have more money in savings, the older they are; until, after a certain age, the amount people have in savings decreases again.*

Any answer which describes the increase up to a certain age and the decrease afterwards is likely to be fine.

The following answer would therefore be acceptable, although it makes the slight mistake of treating the graph as an illustration of a person's savings over a lifetime, rather than as a snapshot of many people's situations at a particular point in time:

As people get older the value of their savings increases, until they reach a certain age, when the value often starts to decrease again.

Marking: 1 mark if correct for upward trend but ignores decline in later-life savings. 0 marks for just 'positive correlation', 'no correlation' or 'no relationship' (though identifying positive correlation up to a certain age and negative after a certain age is fine, if explained). **[2 marks]**

(ii) This is the most likely response:

People save money until they retire, after which point they often have to spend the money they have saved.

Any reasonable answer should be acceptable, so long as it does not involve much guesswork and is not silly.

The following answer would **not** receive a mark:

People save money until they get very old, when it is often stolen from them by their children or by thieves.

The events referred to in this answer are unlikely to affect the *majority* of older people, which would be necessary in order to explain the shape of the graph (if we assume that the data is reasonably representative of the general population).

Marking: Any sensible reason. Small errors in statistical understanding (e.g. implicitly treating graph as the way one person's savings change during life) are likely to be permissible. 0 marks if does not attempt to explain the decline in later-life savings. **[1 mark]**

(b)

positive correlation   negative correlation   (no correlation)

Positive correlation (as x goes up, y goes up) looks reasonable until the right hand end of the chart, where the low values are too numerous to be ignored as outliers.

Negative correlation (as x goes up, y goes down) doesn't fit except at the right hand end.

In other words there is no *overall correlation*, even though it is possible to describe a *relationship* between the age of a person and the value of their savings.

Marking: Correct answer only. **[1 mark]**

9

	Method 1		**Method 2**

$$3x - 5 \leq -\frac{3}{2} + 2x$$

$$3x - 5 \leq -\frac{3}{2} + 2x \qquad 3x - 5 \leq -\frac{3}{2} + 2x$$

Collect terms → Collect x terms to one side

$$x - 5 \leq -\frac{3}{2} \qquad -5 \leq -\frac{3}{2} - x$$

Isolate x term → $-\frac{10}{2} + \frac{3}{2} \leq -x$

$$x \leq -\frac{3}{2} + \frac{10}{2}$$

$$-\frac{7}{2} \leq -x$$

$$x \leq \frac{7}{2} \qquad \frac{7}{2} \geq x \qquad \div -1 \text{ (or } \times -1)$$

both sides. **FLIP SIGN.**

$$x \leq \frac{7}{2}$$

As with most algebra, there are many different ways to the right answer.

The technique here is very similar to any other algebra question. However, I have included **Method 2** in order to demonstrate the most important trick with algebraic inequalities:

- *When you **divide or multiply** by a **negative number**, you **must** swap the direction of the sign.*

You can see this when $-\frac{7}{2} \leq -x$ becomes $\frac{7}{2} \geq x$ (both sides have been divided [or multiplied] by -1).

Otherwise **Method 2** would have given an incorrect answer of $x \geq \frac{7}{2}$.

Marking: 1 mark for good method with minor errors (inequality wrong way round is minor). 0 marks if a major error. **[2 marks]**

---

10 (a) (i)

$$\sqrt{\frac{324}{72}} = \sqrt{\frac{4 \times 81}{2 \times 4 \times 9}} = \sqrt{\frac{\cancel{4} \times 9^3}{\cancel{4} \times \cancel{9} \sqrt{2}}} = \frac{3}{\sqrt{2}}$$

$$\frac{3}{\sqrt{2}} \times \frac{\sqrt{2}}{\sqrt{2}} = \frac{3\sqrt{2}}{2}$$

This could also be written as $\frac{3}{2}\sqrt{2}$.

There are several other routes to the answer, but they all depend on the basic principle that $\sqrt{x} \times \sqrt{x}$ is x. Factorise the numbers to be square rooted into **square numbers** and **primes**, then square root where possible and cancel.

There is one important thing to bear in mind: because the question asks for answers 'in surd form', **you cannot leave a surd (such as $\sqrt{2}$) in the bottom part of the fraction** (the denominator) – this is not allowed in surd form! You must *rationalise the denominator*.

- You can multiply a number by, for example, $\frac{\sqrt{2}}{\sqrt{2}}$ (which equals 1) without changing its value. This allows you to remove a surd from the bottom of a fraction.

- For example, $\frac{1}{\sqrt{5}} = \frac{1}{\sqrt{5}} \times \frac{\sqrt{5}}{\sqrt{5}} = \frac{\sqrt{5}}{5}$.

This is an important principle in maths, which is often tested at GCSE.

Marking: 1 mark if minor errors, e.g. accurate answer not in surd form. **[2 marks]**

(ii)

$$7(\sqrt{7})^{-3} = 7\left(7^{\frac{1}{2}}\right)^{-3} = 7^1 \times 7^{-\frac{3}{2}} = 7^{-\frac{1}{2}} = \frac{1}{\sqrt{7}} = \frac{1}{\sqrt{7}} \times \frac{\sqrt{7}}{\sqrt{7}} = \frac{\sqrt{7}}{7}$$

Because you are asked to give answers in surd form where possible, you need to give your answer as $\frac{\sqrt{7}}{7}$ rather than $7^{-\frac{1}{2}}$.

The solution depends on the following principles, which you need to know by heart:

- $\sqrt{a} = a^{\frac{1}{2}}$ $\qquad\qquad$ $\sqrt{7} = 7^{\frac{1}{2}}$
- $(a^x)^y = a^{xy}$ $\qquad\qquad$ $(7^x)^y = 7^{xy}$
- $a^x \times a^y = a^{x+y}$ $\qquad\qquad$ $7^x \times 7^y = 7^{x+y}$
- $a^{-1} = \frac{1}{a}$ and $a^{-\frac{1}{2}} = \frac{1}{\sqrt{a}}$ $\qquad$ $7^{-1} = \frac{1}{7}$ and $7^{-\frac{1}{2}} = \frac{1}{\sqrt{7}}$
- $a^0 = 1$ $\qquad\qquad$ $7^0 = 1$
- Rationalising the denominator: $\frac{1}{\sqrt{7}} = \frac{1}{\sqrt{7}} \times \frac{\sqrt{7}}{\sqrt{7}} = \frac{\sqrt{7}}{7}$ (see part **(i)**).

Marking: As for **(i)**. **[2 marks]**

(iii)

$$-2.6^0 = -1$$

Anything to the power of 0 equals 1.

Be careful: the question is -26^0, <u>not</u> $(-26)^0$ … which would equal 1, rather than -1.

Marking: Correct answer only. **[1 mark]**

(b)

$$2 \times 9^{-1} = \frac{2}{9}$$

$$\begin{array}{r} 0.22\dot{} \\ 9\overline{)2.0^20} \end{array} \quad \therefore \ 0.\dot{2}$$

It is worth knowing that $\frac{1}{9} = 0.\dot{1}$, $\frac{2}{9} = 0.\dot{2}$, etc.

Always remember that a 'fraction line' means <u>divide</u>. This is a very, very useful fact in many situations.

- Fractions look like a ÷ sign with numbers!

Marking: 1 mark if a very minor error. **[2 marks]**

---

11 Firstly, here is the way that most exam candidates are likely to solve this problem (based on the fact that both triangles are right-angled):

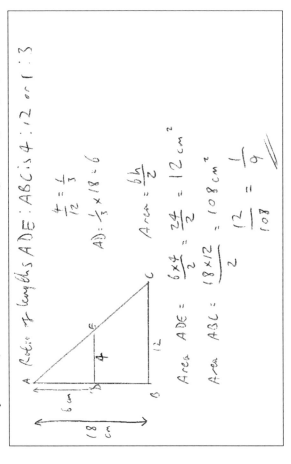

Ratio of lengths ADE : ABC is 4 : 12 or 1 : 3

$$\frac{4}{12} = \frac{1}{3}$$

$$AD): \ \frac{1}{3} \times 18 = 6$$

$$Area = \frac{bh}{2}$$

$$\text{Area } ADE = \frac{6 \times 4}{2} = \frac{24}{2} = 12 \text{ cm}^2$$

$$\text{Area } ABC = \frac{18 \times 12}{2} = 108 \text{ cm}^2$$

$$\frac{12}{108} = \frac{1}{9}$$

- The base of ABC is 3 times as long as the base of ADE.
- Because the triangles are similar, this ratio (1 : 3) will apply to all lengths.
- Using the formula $Area = \frac{Base \times Height}{2}$, find the area of each triangle.
- Express the areas as a fraction and cancel.

However, there is a much more rapid and elegant method available to you. Well done if you used the following approach! If not, see whether you can work out what is going on:

Ratio of lengths ADE : ABC is 4 : 12 or 1 : 3

∴ Ratio of areas is $1^2 : 3^2$ or 1 : 9

$$\frac{1}{9}$$

Yes – it can be done that quickly!

This works because the triangles are similar and because you do not need to find their areas – only the ratio (proportion) of their areas.

The key principle is this:

- When two shapes are similar, *the ratio of their areas is the ratio of their lengths, squared.*

You will also need this knowledge for questions involving scale factors. (For example, a shape which is magnified by a scale factor of 2 increases its area 4 times, because $2^2 = 4$.)

Marking: As for Question 7. **[4 marks]**

---

12 (a)

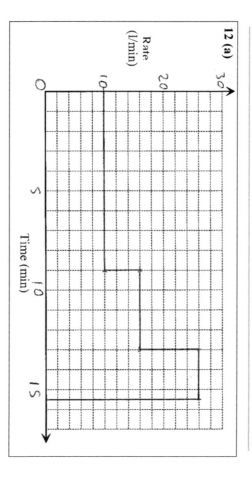

Rate (l/min)

Time (min)

Firstly, you need to select appropriate intervals for the two axes and label them: you already need to know that the rate goes up to 26l/min (both taps together), for example.

The rest is just a matter of being careful and accurate.

A graph without the vertical connecting lines (e.g. at 9 minutes) would probably still get full marks. However, these are useful to show change — for example, that at 15.5 minutes the velocity returns to 0.

Marking: Subtract a mark for each error or missing element. **[3 marks]**

(b)

$$10 \times 9 = 90$$
$$16 \times 4 = 64$$
$$26 \times 2.5 = 65$$
$$219$$

$$219 \, l$$

To find the *volume* of water (which is equivalent to the *displacement* in a velocity/time graph for a journey), you need to find the area beneath the line.

- Multiply the rate by the time for each section.
- Add your results together.
- Don't forget the units of volume (litres).

Marking: 2 marks if a minor error or correct with missing units. 1 mark for correct approach with major/multiple errors. No F.T. marks. **[3 marks]**

---

13 (a)

$$20x^2y^2 - 4y^3 = 4(5x^2y^2 - y^3) = 4y^2(5x^2 - y)$$

Factorising involves *finding the common factor* of the terms in your expression (something which divides into all of them).

- First of all, you can see that 4 goes into both 4 and 20, so you can remove this and place it outside a pair of brackets.
- Next, you can see that y^2 goes into $5x^2y^2$ and into $-y^3$. Take this out as well.

Nothing goes into both $5x^2$ and $-y$, so you have now factorised this expression completely.

Marking: 1 mark if a minor error or incomplete factorisation. **[2 marks]**

(b)

$$(2y-3)(y-5) = 2y^2 - 10y - 3y + 15 = 2y^2 - 13y + 15$$

Expanding an expression is *the opposite of factorising* it.

When you solve a *quadratic equation* (an equation in x^2), you are looking for the points *where the graph cuts across the x axis*: therefore there will usually be two solutions.

(The exceptions are when the graph exactly touches the axis at its base [one solution] and when it is completely above or below the x axis [no solutions].)

- Because the x axis is the line $y = 0$, you solve a quadratic equation by rearranging it to equal 0.

First, notice that every term in $2x^2 + 4x = 70$ can be divided by 2:

$$x^2 + 2x = 35$$

Next, rearrange the equation so that it equals 0, in the form (where $a \neq 0$)
$ax^2 + bx + c = 0$:

$$x^2 + 2x - 35 = 0$$

Now you must *factorise* the equation (the opposite of your method in **(b)**). You need to start with a pair of brackets, in which x^2 has been factorised to give x and x:

$$x^2 + 2x - 35 = 0$$

$$(x \quad)(x \quad)$$

Now think about the −35. There are several ways of making this: -7×5, $7 \times (-5)$, $35 \times (-1)$ and -35×1. However, only some combination of 7 and 5 will give a $2x$ term (because $7 - 5 = 2$):

$$(x \quad 7)(x \quad 5)$$

+5 and −7 would give $-2x$, so you need to use **−5 and +7**:

$$(x + 7)(x - 5) = 0$$

If two things multiply to give 0, then logically at least one of them must equal 0:

- Find your two answers by supposing that $x + 7 = 0$, and solving that; then imagine that $x - 5 = 0$ and do the same.

You need to multiply each term by both terms in the other pair of brackets, like this:

$$(2y - 3)(y - 5)$$

- You can think of this as a face with a small grin, a centre parting and a big chin!

This will give you four terms: $2y^2$, $-10y$, $-3y$ and 15.

You *simplify* this by combining *'like' terms*: $-10y$ and $-3y$ make $-13y$.

Marking: 1 mark if a minor error or a failure to simplify. **[2 marks]**

(c)
$$2x^2 + 4x = 70 \quad \therefore \quad x^2 + 2x = 35$$
$$\therefore \quad x^2 + 2x - 35 = 0$$
$$(x + 7)(x - 5) = 0$$
$$\text{Where } x - 5 = 0$$
$$x = 5$$
$$\text{Where } x + 7 = 0$$
$$x = -7$$

As you probably know, a graph where the highest power of x is x^2 (and where x^2 and y have the same sign: not, for example, y and $-3x^2$), looks roughly like this:

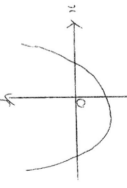

- (If x^2 had a negative coefficient, the graph would have the same basic shape, but be upside down.)

Marking: 2 marks if minor errors. 1 mark for some understanding but a bit of a mess. N.B. a method which does not involve factorising loses 1 mark automatically. **[3 marks]**

Sometimes the solutions to a quadratic equation are not whole numbers. In that situation, you will need to use the quadratic formula:

For an equation in the form $ax^2 + bx + c = 0$, it follows that $x = \frac{-b \pm \sqrt{b^2 - 4ac}}{2a}$

You will practise this method later, and in the *RSL* GCSE calculator papers.

---

14 (a)

$$1 = 0.1 + 0.325 + 2x + x + 0.1 + 0.025$$
$$= 0.2 + 0.35 + 3x$$
$$\therefore 1 = 0.55 + 3x$$
$$\therefore 3x = 1 - 0.55 = 0.45$$
$$\therefore x = \frac{0.45}{3} = \underline{0.15}$$

Because it is certain that any chocolate bar from my cupboard has one of the weights in the table, *all the probabilities must add up to 1*.

- This calculation is only possible because the ranges are **exclusive**: they do not overlap.

Once all the numbers have been tidied up, you can find x with a simple bit of algebra.

Marking: 1 mark if a minor number error. 0 marks if multiple errors. **[2 marks]**

(b)

$$0.1 + 0.325 + 2x = 0.1 + 0.325 + 0.3 = 0.4 + 0.325 = \underline{0.725}$$

You need to substitute (insert) your answer to part (a) in order to solve this.

If your answer to (a) was wrong, but your working here is correct, you will still get the marks for this question (follow-through marking – see **Introduction page**).

Marking: As for (a). FT marks. **[2 marks]**

(c)

$$13\overline{)0.325} \quad \frac{0.025}{} \quad \frac{1}{0.025} = \frac{1000}{25} = \underline{40}$$

The probability of a chocolate bar weighing 40g to 50g is 0.325. We know from the question that this is equivalent to 13 chocolate bars.

- Divide 0.325 by 13, to give 0.025 (which represents one bar).
- Now you need to find out how many times 0.025 goes into 1.

Notice the method for removing the decimal point before cancelling: multiplying the top and bottom of the fraction (the numerator and denominator) by 1000.

Marking: 1 mark for largely correct method with minor errors. **[2 marks]**

15

$$f(x) = 5 - 3x$$
$$\therefore fg(x) = 5 - 3[g(x)]$$
$$fg(x) = 7$$
$$\therefore 7 = 5 - 3[g(x)]$$
$$2 = -3[g(x)]$$
$$\underline{\underline{-\tfrac{2}{3} = g(x)}}$$

This is an easy problem pretending to be difficult – a biscuit served with chopsticks.

A function of x equals $5 - 3x$. The same function f of another function, $g(x)$, equals 7: $fg(x) = 7$

A function of x equals $5 - 3x$ tells you that you can put a value of x in the expression to the right of the '=' sign. For example, $f(2) = 5 - (3 \times 2) = -1$

You can do this with $g(x)$:

$$fg(x) = 5 - 3[g(x)]$$

But we know that $fg(x)$ is the same as 7:

$$7 = 5 - 3[g(x)]$$

You can solve this, as in the example, to find that $g(x)$ equals $\dfrac{2}{-3}$, which you would usually write as $-\dfrac{2}{3}$

Marking: 1 mark if evidence of some understanding. **[2 marks]**

16

S. area:	9 : 25
Length (e.g. radius):	3 : 5 ← $\sqrt{9}$: $\sqrt{25}$
Mass/Volume:	27 : 125 ← 3^3 : 5^3

$$27 : 125$$
$$540 : V$$

$$\frac{540}{27} = 20 \qquad 125 \times 20 = 2500$$

$$\underline{\underline{\text{Mass of } V = 2500\,kg}}$$

- The second half of the solution could also be approached by setting up and solving an equation:

$$\frac{540}{27} = \frac{V}{125}$$

This question uses the same principle as the second solution to **Question 11**, but takes it further.

To start with, it is important to recognise that mass increases and decreases in proportion to volume: 2cm³ of a material weighs twice as much as 1cm³ of the same material. Therefore you can treat the masses in this question exactly like volumes.

Surface area is a squared measure (cm², m², etc.), so you can go from the ratio of surface areas to the ratio of lengths (cm, m) *by square rooting each number:*

$$\sqrt{9} : \sqrt{25} \text{ gives } 3 : 5$$

You can find the ratio of volumes (or masses) *by cubing the ratio of lengths:*

$$3^3 : 5^3 \text{ gives } 27 : 125$$

Use this ratio to find the mass of **V**.

- It is difficult to go directly from the ratio of surface areas to the ratio of volumes: you should find the ratio of lengths first.

Marking: 3 marks if minor errors. 2 marks for a decent attempt but significantly wrong working. 1 mark for a vaguely reasonable method with major errors. **[4 marks]**

---

17 (a) (i)

$$\overrightarrow{XT} = \underline{b} + \underline{c} \quad \text{or} \quad \overrightarrow{XT} = 2\underline{a} - \underline{c}$$

- To show that a single letter is a vector when handwriting, you should underline it.

Because T and R are midpoints, you can get from X to T by going along **b** and up **c**, or up **a** twice (to Y) and down **c** (to T).

- If you go the 'wrong way' along a vector, you need to show this with a '-' sign.

Marking: Correct answer only. Permit missing underlines. **[1 mark]**

(ii)

$$\overrightarrow{ZR} = -\underline{b} + \underline{a} \quad \text{or} \quad \overrightarrow{ZR} = 2\underline{c} - \underline{a}$$

The method here is the same as for part (i).

Marking: As for (i). **[1 mark]**

(c)

$$\overrightarrow{RT} = \underline{a} - \underline{c}$$

$$\overrightarrow{XZ} = 2\underline{a} - 2\underline{c} = 2(\underline{a} - \underline{c}) = 2(\overrightarrow{RT})$$

This question is *much* easier than it looks, if you consider all possible routes. Essentially, you need to **find the routes from R to T and from X to Z** and **compare them.**

The solution above shows that the routes *contain the same mixture of **a** and **c**:*

(a – c).

- This means that they are parallel.

The solution also shows that $\overrightarrow{XZ}$ is *double the size of* $\overrightarrow{RT}$.

- This means that it is twice as long.

Marking: 2 marks for correct working but result not clearly demonstrated (answer needs to reach at least $\overrightarrow{XZ} = 2\underline{a} - 2\underline{c}$ for 3 marks). 1 mark for some attempt at proof but errors or incomplete. **[3 marks]**

18 (a)

$$\text{area} = \pi r^2$$

$$x^2 + y^2 = r^2$$

$$\therefore 16\pi = \pi r^2 \qquad \therefore x^2 + y^2 = 16$$

$$\therefore \sqrt{16} = r = 4$$

We know the area of this circle (16π), and of course the area of a circle is given by $A = \pi r^2$.

Therefore you can work out r, the radius, of the circle.

Because the equation of a circle with centre (0 , 0) is in the form $x^2 + y^2 = r^2$, the equation of *this* circle is $x^2 + y^2 = 4^2$, simplified to $x^2 + y^2 = 16$.

Marking: 1 mark if shows recognition of $x^2 + y^2 = r^2$ but rest is a mess. 2 marks if a half-decent attempt to combine with $A = \pi r^2$. **[3 marks]**

(b) The negative reciprocal of $\frac{4}{3}$ is $-\frac{3}{4}$, so $-\frac{3}{4}$ **is the gradient of the tangent**. This makes sense, because the line runs downwards from left to right, so must have a negative gradient.

Using the standard equation for a straight line, $y - y_1 = m(x - x_1)$, you can find the equation of the tangent by inserting the coordinates (6 , 2) in place of x_1 and y_1 respectively.

Make sure that you simplify the equation to use the smallest possible integers (whole numbers), and that you write it in the form $ay = bx + c$, as requested. The example shows two convenient ways of doing this.

Marking: 4 marks for correct answer in wrong format / not integers. Higher integers e.g. $8y = -6x + 52$ are acceptable for 5 marks. 3 marks for minor errors. 2 marks for frequent or major errors. 1 mark for some understanding but negligible correct working. **[5 marks]**

END OF PAPER 1 SOLUTIONS   **TOTAL 80 MARKS**

To find the equation of a straight line, you need to know **its gradient** and the coordinates of **a point on the line**. We know from the question that the given point (6 , 2) is on the tangent line, so we only need to find its gradient.

The vital principle is this:

- The gradient of a tangent to a circle at a certain point *is at right angles to the gradient of the radius* where it meets that same point.

In other words, *the gradient of the radius is the **negative reciprocal** of the gradient of the tangent*, and vice versa. (See **Question 5** above for a discussion of negative reciprocals.)

Find the gradient of the radius which runs through (3 , −2) and (6 , 2) using the formula $Gradient = \frac{Change\ in\ y}{Change\ in\ x}$ or $\frac{y_2 - y_1}{x_2 - x_1}$:

$$\frac{2 - (-2)}{6 - 3} = \frac{4}{3}$$

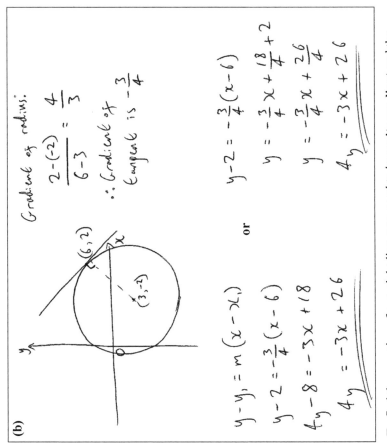

Gradient of radius:

$$\frac{2 - (-2)}{6 - 3} = \frac{4}{3}$$

∴ Gradient of tangent is $-\frac{3}{4}$

$$y - y_1 = m(x - x_1)$$

$$y - 2 = -\frac{3}{4}(x - 6)$$

$$4y - 8 = -3x + 18$$

$$4y = -3x + 26$$

or

$$y - 2 = -\frac{3}{4}(x - 6)$$

$$y = -\frac{3}{4}x + \frac{18}{4} + 2$$

$$y = -\frac{3}{4}x + \frac{26}{4}$$

$$4y = -3x + 26$$

Paper 2 (80 marks)

If you wish to complete this paper in timed conditions, allow 1hr 30mins.

1   ABC is a triangle.

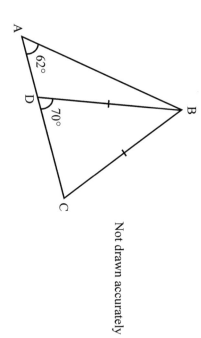

Not drawn accurately

Find angle ABC.

.... [2]

2   Solve the following inequality, representing the solution on the number line below. You must show your working.

$17 - 2x < 7$

-7 -6 -5 -4 -3 -2 -1 0 1 2 3 4 5 6 7 x

[4]

3   Two cyclists, Chris and Victoria, ride from London to Brighton. They both cycle as fast as they can.

The journey takes Chris 4 hours without stopping, at an average speed of 24.5km/h.

Victoria rides the same route as Chris. She also takes 4 hours, including a 30 minute pause for lunch.

(a)   Work out Victoria's average riding speed, not including her lunch break.

.... [4]

(b)   Bradley believes these figures demonstrate that Victoria is a better cyclist than Chris.

Basing your answer on the information in the question and/or your answer to part (a), give a reason why he might be right, and a reason why he might be wrong.

.... [2]

4   Karen and Ollie each drop a number of slices of toast.

Karen always holds her toast exactly the same way before dropping it.

Ollie always holds his toast exactly the same way before dropping it.

They record how many slices land marmalade side down and how many land marmalade side up.

	Slices landing 'marmalade down'	Slices landing 'marmalade up'
Karen	110	44
Ollie	106	159

(a)   Based on these results:

(i)   Estimate the probability that Ollie will drop a piece of toast marmalade side down.

.... [2]

(ii)   Estimate the probability that Karen will drop a piece of toast marmalade side down.

.... [2]

(b)   Suggest a likely reason why Ollie and Karen might have such different results. Explain your answer clearly.

.... [2]

(c)   Ollie and Karen each drop a piece of toast at the same time.

Basing your answer on the information in the table, estimate the probability that one piece will land marmalade-down and the other marmalade-up.

.... [4]

5   I record the amount that I spend on diesel for my car every month.

In June I spent £195.50, which was 15% less than in May.

(a)   My accountant tries to work out what I spent in May.

This is her working:

$100\% + 15\% = 115\% = 1.15$

$195.5 \times 1.15 = 224.825$

224.825 to 2 d.p. gives £224.83

My accountant has made a mistake.

Explain in your own words why her method is wrong.

.... [2]

(b)   Calculate what I really spent on diesel in May.

.... **[4]**

6   Work out $4\frac{2}{5} \div 2\frac{3}{4}$

Give your answer as a mixed number in its simplest form.

.... **[3]**

7   (a)   Find the gradient of the line $y + 3x = 5$

.... **[2]**

(b)   Another line passes through the point $(28 , 1)$ and is perpendicular
to the line $y + 3x = 5$

Find the coordinates of the point where the two lines intersect.

.... **[5]**

8 Work out the value of $(4.5 \times 10^{-9}) \times (4 \times 10^6)$.

Give your answer in standard form.

.... **[3]**

9 An expanded polystyrene sphere has a radius of 14.8cm.

(a) Using appropriate rounding or estimates, show that the volume of the sphere is likely to be in the range $0.0135\text{m}^3 \leq V \leq 0.0145\text{m}^3$.

[The volume V of a sphere is given by $V = \frac{4}{3}\pi r^3$]

[2]

(b) The density of expanded polystyrene is 20.5kg/m^3. Using this exact value, and the information from (a), find a suitable estimate for the mass of the sphere.

.... **[2]**

10 Evaluate $125^{-\frac{2}{3}}$

.... **[3]**

11   Write down five numbers which have

- a median of 3
- a mode of 2
- a mean of 6
- a range of 12

.... [3]

12    $\frac{3\sqrt{90}}{2} - \frac{\sqrt{20}}{\sqrt{10}}$ simplifies to give $\frac{\sqrt{2}}{k}(9\sqrt{5} - k)$ where k is an integer.

Find the value of k.

.... [4]

13 Farieda took 11 mock exams.

Here are her marks out of 100:

54   60   60   65   72   74
76   79   85   90   92

(a) Draw a box plot for this information:

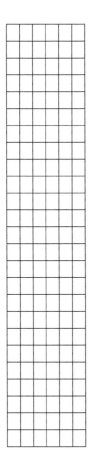

[3]

(b) Nicholas took the same 11 mock exams.

- The median of his marks was 79.
- The interquartile range of his marks was 28.
- The range of his marks was 41.

Who was more consistent, Farieda or Nicholas?

Give a reason for your answer.

.... [2]

14 (a) Expand and simplify $\left(\sqrt{5} - \sqrt{4}\right)\left(\sqrt{4} + \sqrt{5}\right)$

.... [3]

(b) Rewrite the following numbers in order, from smallest to largest.

$$0.4 \qquad 1.2^2 \qquad \frac{4}{11} \qquad \frac{1}{3} \qquad \sqrt{0.1} \qquad \frac{5}{4}$$

.... [2]

15 **(a)** Sketch the graph of $y = \cos x$ for $0° \leq x \leq 360°$.

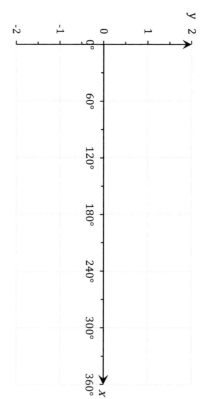

(b) **(i)** Write down the coordinates of the <u>minimum</u> point of

$y = \cos(x - 35)$ for $0° \leq x \leq 360°$

....

[2]

(ii) Write down the coordinates of the <u>maximum</u> point of

$y = 4 - \cos x$ for $0° \leq x \leq 360°$

....

[2]

16 PQR is a right-angled triangle with vertices **P** $(3, 1)$, **Q** $(k, 7)$ and **R** $(9, 3)$.

Angle QPR is the right angle.

Find the equation of the line which passes through **Q** and **R**.

You should give your answer in the form $ay = bx + c$ where a, b and c are the smallest possible integers (closest to 0).

....

[5]

17 In the following diagram, two small circles, **A** and **B**, have been drawn inside a large circle. The large circle is the border of the diagram.

The centre of each small circle lies on the diameter of the large circle.

Circle **A** has half the diameter of circle **B**.

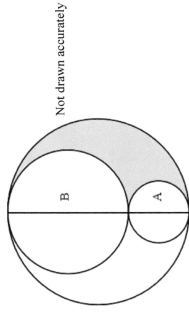

Not drawn accurately

What fraction of the diagram has been shaded?

.... [4]

END   **TOTAL FOR PAPER 2 IS 80 MARKS**

1

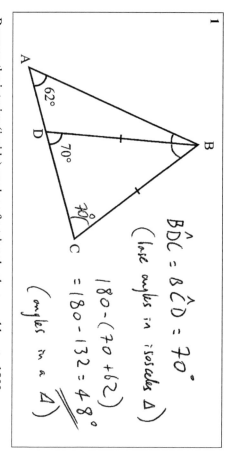

Because the interior (inside) angles of a triangle always add up to 180°, once we know two angles, we can work out the third by subtracting.

- We know that angle BAC is 62°.
- Angle ACB must be 70°, because the lines BD and BC are of equal length (as shown by the marks on these two lines): *the base angles in an isosceles triangle are equal.*
- Therefore you can find angle ABC by subtracting 62° and 70° from 180°.

Some people might follow a less direct (but equally correct) approach:

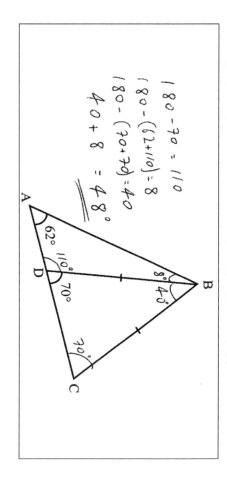

$$B\hat{D}C = B\hat{C}D = 70°$$
(base angles in isosceles △)

$$180 - (70 + 62)$$
$$= (180 - 132 = 48°$$
(angles in a △)

- Because there are 180° in a half turn (in a straight line, you could say), the angle ADB must be 110°: $180 - 70 = 110$
- Using this information, and the fact that angle BCD must be 70°, you can work out the two interior angles at **B**.
- Finally, you add your answers (40° and 8°) together.

It can be helpful when writing your working to **briefly indicate the reasons for your main steps** (as in the first example above). This demonstrates good working to the examiner.

Marking: 1 mark if a minor error. Permit missing units (degrees). **[2 marks]**

$$180 - 70 = 110$$
$$180 - (62 + 110) = 8$$
$$180 - (70 + 70) = 40$$
$$40 + 8 = 48°$$

2

Representing a simple inequality on a number line is easy if you remember three rules:

- If the solution is 'greater than' (>) or 'less than' (<) (as in this question), you use an open circle ○.
- If the solution is 'greater than or equal to' (≥) or 'less than or equal to' (≤), you use a filled circle ●.
- On the number line, your line should go over *the area which might include x*, and have an arrow if this continues beyond the number line.

You can draw your line along or above the number line, so long as it is clear.

For a discussion of solving inequalities, see the solution to **Paper 1 Question 9**.

Remember that *when you multiply or divide by a negative number, the inequality sign must reverse* (see **Paper 1, Question 9**). You can see this in the right hand solution above.

$$17 - 2x < 7$$
$$17 < 2x + 7$$
$$10 < 2x$$
$$5 < x$$

or

$$17 - 2x < 7$$
$$-2x < -10$$
$$-x < -5$$
$$x > 5$$

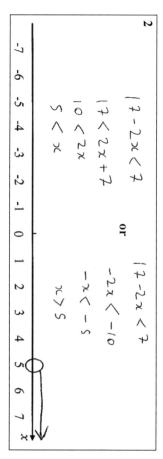

(b) *He might be right, because Victoria's average riding speed is faster than Chris's.*

He might be wrong, because Chris manages a speed which is only 3.5km/h slower, despite not having a 30 minute break.

This is testing your ability to reach real-world judgements based on data.

An equivalent point would also be acceptable:

- For example, you could also say that *he might be right because Victoria rides the same distance in less time.*

Your answer **must respond to the given information**: saying, for example, that one cyclist is *slower and safer, therefore better* would **not** be relevant.

Marking: 1 mark for why right, 1 mark for why wrong. Reasons must contain some degree of explanation, and must respond to information from the question and/or part **(a)**. **[2 marks]**

---

4 (a) (i)

$$106 + 159 = 265 \qquad \frac{106}{265} = \frac{2}{5}$$

Remember that you **find experimental probability** by writing the number of 'marmalade down' results as the numerator (the top of the fraction), while the denominator is *the total number of attempts.*

- **Don't** make the mistake of trying to work out $\frac{106}{159}$.

You will lose marks in a question like this if you forget to simplify (reduce) your fraction. This one is tricky, because the only common factor of 106 and 265 is a prime number, 53, which may not be obvious.

Marking: 1 mark if a minor error or not simplified. No marks if uses $\frac{106}{159}$. **[2 marks]**

Marking: 2 marks available for working; 2 marks for number line. Working: 1 mark if a couple of minor errors e.g. wrong inequality sign or negative/positive number error. Number line: Mark this based on the answer obtained in working, even if wrong. 1 mark if line in correct place but filled circle used and/or arrow missing. **[4 marks]**

3 (a)

$D = S \times T$

i) $= 24.5 \times 4 = 98 \, km$

Vic's time: $4 - 0.5 = 3.5$

$S = \frac{D}{T} = \frac{98}{3.5} \, \frac{(\times 2)}{(\times 2)} = \frac{196}{7} = 28$

$28 \, km/h$

The speed/distance/time triangle, shown above, is worth learning:

- Cover the value (**S**, **D** or **T**) you are trying to find.
- This can be found from the other two values, where the horizontal line means divide, and the vertical line means multiply.

Therefore:

- $Speed = \frac{Distance}{Time}$
- $Distance = Speed \times Time$
- $Time = \frac{Distance}{Speed}$

You can find Chris's distance (which is the same as Victoria's) by multiplying his speed and his time. This gives 98km.

Victoria stops for half an hour, so her riding time is 3.5 hours.

Using $S = \frac{D}{T}$, we can now find her average speed.

Marking: 3 marks if minor error; 2 marks if good attempt but multiple/larger errors; 1 mark if correct SDT equation used but rest is a disaster. **[4 marks]**

Experimental probability is probability *derived from an experiment*, as in this case; **theoretical probability** is *worked out from first principles*.

- For example, you could **experimentally** estimate the probability that ten coin tosses all give heads by tossing a coin ten times, repeating this test many thousands of times, and recording how often the required result does and does not occur.

- You could find the same probability **theoretically** by calculating $\left(\frac{1}{2}\right)^{10}$.

(ii)

$$110 + 44 = 154 \qquad \frac{110}{154} = \frac{10}{14} = \frac{5}{7}$$

The same method applies here. Don't look for $\frac{110}{44}$.

Marking: As for **(i)**: do not allow marks for $\frac{110}{44}$. **[2 marks]**

(b)

- *It is likely that Ollie and Karen each hold their slices in different ways before dropping them, affecting how many times the toast rotates.*

or

- *It is likely that one person is taller than the other. Each slice will have more time to turn over when dropped by the taller person.*

or

- *It is possible that Karen and Ollie hold their toast slices different ways up, making different landing positions more likely.*

Any sensible answer is likely to receive two marks. However, it is wise to add a short explanation, because the question asks you to 'explain clearly'.

Marking: Any sensible answer. Needs clear explanation of why would affect results for 2nd mark. **[2 marks]**

(c) **Method 1**

$$(\text{Ollie up} \times \text{Karen down}) + (\text{Ollie down} \times \text{Karen up})$$
$$= \left(\frac{3}{5} \times \frac{5}{7}\right) + \left(\frac{2}{5} \times \frac{2}{7}\right)$$
$$= \frac{15}{35} + \frac{4}{35}$$
$$= \frac{19}{35}$$

- When two events **A** and **B** are independent (they don't affect each other), the probability that both happen is **A × B**.

This rule applies here, because *whether one person's slice lands marmalade-down is not affected by whether the other person's does*: to make sure of this, the slices are dropped at the same time.

There are two possible ways that one slice might land marmalade-down and one slice marmalade-up:

- Ollie's slice might land with the marmalade down and Karen's with the marmalade up.
- Karen's slice might land with the marmalade down and Ollie's with the marmalade up.

To find the answer using the method above, you need to *find the probability of each of these options*, before **adding them together**.

Method 2

$$1 - (\text{both up} + \text{both down})$$
$$= 1 - \left(\frac{3}{5} \times \frac{2}{7} + \frac{2}{5} \times \frac{5}{7}\right) = 1 - \left(\frac{6}{35} + \frac{10}{35}\right) = 1 - \frac{16}{35} = \frac{19}{35}$$

This method is a little bit tidier, because you end up with two fractions with the same denominator.

Think about it like this:

Here is how my accountant **should** have done it:

(b)

There are two main steps here (and the diagram above might be a worth remembering for this sort of question):

A: The unknown May amount was decreased by 15%, which means that the June amount is 85% of the figure for May.

$$May \times 0.85 = June$$

B: If $May \times 0.85 = June$, then

$$May = \frac{June}{0.85}$$

Substituting the figure for June,

$$\frac{195.5}{0.85} = £230$$

Remember:

- When you need to turn a fraction into a decimal value, you must **divide**.

Marking: 3 marks if a minor calculation error. 2 marks if broadly correct method but working is poor. 1 mark if some basic understanding but not much else. 0 marks if repeats the accountant's mistake. **[4 marks]**

- The probability that one piece of toast lands marmalade-up and one piece marmalade-down is the same as *the probability that both pieces don't land in the same way*.

If the total probability of all possible outcomes is 1:

- Add together the probability that the slices both land marmalade-up and the probability that both slices land marmalade-down.
- Subtract your result from 1.

Marking: 1 mark if forgets a significant part of the calculation. 2 marks if reasonably structured answer but actual working is a dog's dinner. 3 marks if a minor error or two and/or fractions not fully simplified. **[4 marks]**

5 (a) *Her method is wrong because she has found 15% of the June amount, which will be less than 15% of the original, larger amount in May.*

or

Her method is wrong because the June amount is 85% of the May amount, but the May amount is not 115% of the June amount.

In other words, if the June amount is 15% less than the May amount, this means that *the May amount has been reduced by 15%* - and you cannot get back to this value by increasing the June figure by 15%, because *this would involve finding 15% of a smaller number*.

Be careful to **explain in words**: this question is **not** asking you to find the correct value as in part **(b)**.

- Good exam technique involves **reading through the entire question** before beginning it.

Marking: Needs a clear explanation for 2 marks. 1 mark for correct concept, inaccurately or unclearly explained. **[2 marks]**

6

$$4\frac{2}{5} \div 2\frac{3}{4} = \frac{22}{5} \div \frac{11}{4} = \frac{22}{5} \times \frac{4}{11} = \frac{8}{5} = 1\frac{3}{5}$$

When performing division or multiplication with mixed numbers, it is helpful to turn them into top-heavy (improper) fractions at the beginning.

As a reminder of how to do this, look at the first number from the solution above (expanded to show intermediate steps):

$$4\frac{2}{5} = 1+1+1+1+\frac{2}{5} = \frac{5}{5}+\frac{5}{5}+\frac{5}{5}+\frac{5}{5}+\frac{2}{5} = \frac{22}{5}$$

You can take a shortcut like this:

$2 + 20 = 22$

$4 \times 5 = 20$

When you **divide by a fraction**, you turn it over and multiply:

$A \div \frac{x}{y} = A \times \frac{y}{x}$, or in the solution above, $\frac{22}{5} \div \frac{11}{4} = \frac{22}{5} \times \frac{4}{11}$

If it is hard to see why this should be the case, look at this example:

$$10 \times \frac{1}{2} = 5 = 10 \div \frac{2}{1}$$

Marking: 2 marks if minor error. 1 mark if flips second fraction but rest is wrong. If wrong and does not flip second fraction and multiply (or use equivalent method), 0 marks. **[3 marks]**

---

7 (a)

$$y + 3x = 5 \qquad \therefore y = -3x + 5$$
$$y = mx + c$$
$$\therefore m = -3$$

Because $y = mx + c$ gives us the gradient m as the coefficient of x, you must ensure the equation is in this form so that you can read off the gradient.

- Rearrange to **make y the subject**, then **find the number in front of x**.
- Don't forget the negative sign!

Marking: 1 mark if missing negative sign. **[2 marks]**

(b)

Gradient: $-\dfrac{1}{(-3)} = \dfrac{1}{3}$ $(x_1, y_1) = (28, 1)$

$$y - y_1 = m(x - x_1)$$
$$\therefore y - 1 = \frac{1}{3}(x - 28)$$

or

$$3y - 3 = x - 28$$
$$3y = x - 25$$
$$y = \frac{x - 25}{3}$$

$$y = \frac{x}{3} - \frac{28}{3} + 1$$
$$y = \frac{x}{3} - \frac{25}{3}$$

(A) $y = -3x + 5$

(B) $y = \dfrac{x - 25}{3}$

Substitute: $-3x + 5 = \dfrac{x - 25}{3}$
$$-9x + 15 = x - 25$$
$$15 = 10x - 25$$
$$40 = 10x$$
$$4 = x$$

$$y = -3x + 5$$
$$= -3 \times 4 + 5 = -12 + 5 = -7 \qquad (4, -7)$$

There are two main steps here.

Step 1: Find the equation of the new line.

First of all you need its gradient. The new line is perpendicular to $y + 3x = 5$ (or $y = -3x + 5$), so its gradient will be the negative reciprocal of -3 (from part (a)).

- For negative reciprocals, see **Paper 1, Questions 5** and **18(b)**.

Therefore its gradient is $\frac{1}{3}$.

We know that the new line passes through $(28, 1)$.

- When you know a point (x_1, y_1) on a line and its gradient m, you can use the following formula to find its equation:

$$y - y_1 = m(x - x_1)$$

If you don't know this already, learn it! It could easily make a grade or two of difference to your GCSE result.

Inserting $(28, 1)$ and the gradient $\frac{1}{3}$, we get $y - 1 = \frac{1}{3}(x - 28)$, which can be rearranged to give $y = \frac{x-25}{3}$ or $y = \frac{x}{3} - \frac{25}{3}$

Step 2: Find the point of intersection

Now you need to find the point where the two lines meet.

You do this by solving the equations simultaneously.

The easiest method here is **substitution.**

- Make both equations equal y (if you haven't already):

$$y = -3x + 5$$

$$y = \frac{x - 25}{3}$$

- Rewrite them together:

Because

$$-3x + 5 = y = \frac{x - 25}{3}$$

therefore

$$-3x + 5 = \frac{x - 25}{3}$$

(You will probably want to skip the first ('because') step above: I have included it to make things clear.)

- Now you solve the equation $-3x + 5 = \frac{x-25}{3}$, giving a result of $x = 4$.
- Go back to either of your '$y =$' equations and substitute $x = 4$:

$$y = -3x + 5 \text{ so } y = -3 \times 4 + 5 = -12 + 5 = -7$$

- Finally, don't forget to give your answer as a pair of coordinates:

$$(4, -7)$$

> **Marking:** 4 marks if minor calculation error. 3 marks if multiple minor errors or a slight mistake in method. 2 marks if some good things but the method is substantially wrong. 1 mark if understands need to compare two equations in some way, but not much else. Allow F.T. of gradient from **(a)**. **[5 marks]**

8

$$\left(4.5 \times 10^{-9}\right) \times \left(4 \times 10^6\right) = 4.5 \times 4 \times 10^{-9} \times 10^6$$

$$= \left(18 \times 10^{(-9+6)}\right) = 18 \times 10^{-3} = 1.8 \times 10^{-2}$$

To multiply numbers in standard form:

- Remove the brackets.
- Multiply the numbers without indices (here, 4.5 and 4).
- Multiply the numbers with indices by <u>adding the indices</u> (see **Paper 1, Question 10(a)(ii)**):

$$x^y \times x^z = x^{y+z}$$

- <u>Ensure that your answer is in standard form.</u>

The last step is important, and easy to forget.

18×10^{-3} is **not** in standard form, because in standard form the first number must be <u>less than 10 and greater than or equal to 1</u>.

Therefore you need to re-write it as 1.8×10^{-2}: moving the decimal point one place to the left (from 18.0 to 1.8) is balanced by changing 10^{-3} into 10^{-2}, meaning that the size of the number does not change:

$$18 \times 10^{-3} = (1.8 \times 10^1) \times 10^{-3} = 1.8 \times 10^{-2} \ (= 0.018)$$

Marking: 2 marks if gives 18×10^{-3} as final answer or if answer in standard form but minor error creates wrong answer. 1 mark if a good attempt but bigger mistakes. **[3 marks]**

9 (a)

You need to find an approximate value which is within the given range.

In the example, I have labelled the main steps **A**, **B** and **C** and **D**.

$\approx$ means 'is approximately equal to'.

A: You will probably want to round π (3.141...) down to 3. Therefore you need to round 14.8 up to 15.

- *You should not round only one of these*, or you will distort your answer unnecessarily. It would be inconsistent to round π but not the radius, and this would be likely to lose marks.

However, any reasonable estimates which give a result in the requested range are likely to be accepted.

B: Use your estimates with the given formula for the volume of a sphere.

C/D: There are 1,000,000 cm³ in a m³ (really!), so you must divide your value from **B** by 1,000,000.

Alternatively, you could write your estimates in metres in step **A**, allowing you to skip **C** and **D**:

$$\frac{4}{3} \times 3 \times 0.15^3 = 4 \times 0.003375 = 0.0135m^3$$

Marking: Any answer in the requested range is acceptable, so long as it is supported by accurate working from reasonable estimates. 1 mark if good estimates but moderate errors in working, or if unwise estimates followed by strong working. **[2 marks]**

(b)

$$Mass = Density \times Volume$$

You may be tempted to further approximate your value for volume, but this would risk adding unnecessary inaccuracy.

You can deal with the existing decimals by performing a straightforward multiplication, as shown in the example.

- If you do approximate further, you will be safe so long as your approximations are reasonable and your answer lands in the range of masses derived from the range of volumes given in **(a)** (see mark scheme).

Equivalent answers in kg are likely to be acceptable, though grams are more appropriate here.

Marking: Based on the range of volumes indicated in **(a)**, any answer between 276.75g and 297.25g is acceptable here. Remove a mark for minor errors, or for unwise further rounding of volume which distorts an otherwise good solution out of this range. Max 1 mark if 20.5 is rounded. **[2 marks]**

10

$$125^{-\frac{2}{3}} = \left(125^{\frac{1}{3}}\right)^{-2} = \left(\sqrt[3]{125}\right)^{-2} = 5^{-2} = \frac{1}{5^2} = \frac{1}{25}$$

or

$$125^{-\frac{2}{3}} = \left(125^{-\frac{1}{3}}\right)^2 = \left(\frac{1}{\sqrt[3]{125}}\right)^2 = \left(\frac{1}{5}\right)^2 = \frac{1}{25}$$

or (not recommended)

$$125^{-\frac{2}{3}} = 125^{-\frac{1}{3}} \times 125^{-\frac{1}{3}} = \frac{1}{\sqrt[3]{125}} \times \frac{1}{\sqrt[3]{125}} = \frac{1}{5} \times \frac{1}{5} = \frac{1}{25}$$

$$125^{-\frac{2}{3}} = \left(125^2\right)^{-\frac{1}{3}} = 15625^{-\frac{1}{3}} = \frac{1}{\sqrt[3]{15625}} = \frac{1}{25}$$

The rules used here are outlined in the solution to **Paper 1, Question 10(a)(ii)**.

The final method involves finding the cube root of 15,625, which is why it might not be the best choice!

• Where there is more than one operation to perform, **it is usually easiest to make a number smaller before you make it larger**: cube root 125 before squaring.

Marking: 2 marks if minor error; 1 mark if some good ideas; 0 marks if way off track. **[3 marks]**

11

Ⓑ 2 Ⓐ 2 Ⓓ 3 Ⓒ 9 14

① $6 \times 5 = 30$
$30 - (14 + 3 + 2 + 2)$
$= 30 - 21 = 9$

A, B, C and **D** have been added to show the steps which solve the problem most easily.

A: 3 is the median. Simple!

B: Because 2 is the mode (the most frequent number), there must be at least two 2s; because of the 3, there cannot be more than two.

C: Because the range (the difference between the smallest and largest numbers) is 12, the largest number must be 14.

D: Because the mean is 6, the total of all the numbers must be $6 \times 5 = 30$. Therefore the missing number must be 9.

Marking: Consult bullet points in question: 2 marks if three correct, 1 mark if two correct, 0 marks if one or none correct. **[3 marks]**

12

$$\frac{3\sqrt{90}}{2} - \frac{\sqrt{20}}{\sqrt{10}} = \frac{3\sqrt{9 \times 5 \times 2}}{2} - Ⓐ\sqrt{\frac{4 \times 5}{2 \times 5}} = \frac{3 \times 3\sqrt{5}\sqrt{2}}{2} - \frac{2\sqrt{5}}{\sqrt{2}\sqrt{5}}$$

$$= \frac{9\sqrt{5}\sqrt{2}}{2} - \frac{2}{\sqrt{2}} = Ⓒ\frac{9\sqrt{5}\sqrt{2}\sqrt{2} - 4}{2\sqrt{2}} = \frac{9 \times 2\sqrt{5} - 4}{2\sqrt{2}}$$

$$= \frac{\cancel{2}\left(9\sqrt{5} - 2\right)}{\cancel{2}\sqrt{2}} = \frac{9\sqrt{5} - 2}{\sqrt{2}} \times \frac{\sqrt{2}}{\sqrt{2}} = \frac{\sqrt{2}\left(9\sqrt{5} - 2\right)}{2} \ Ⓓ$$

$$\underline{k = 2}$$

A: Factorise the numbers inside square roots:

• Find any factors which are square numbers (here, 9 and 4).
• Reduce the rest to primes (here, 2 and 5).

B: Square root the square numbers.

Cancel and simplify as far as you can within each separate fraction.

C: Subtract the fractions:

$$\frac{P}{Q} - \frac{R}{S} = \frac{PS - RQ}{QS}$$

Cancel and simplify as far as you can.

D: Rationalise the denominator (see **Paper 1, Question 10(a)(i)**).

• **Always answer the question!** Don't forget to state the value of k.

Marking: 3 marks if answer not quite right because of minor error, or doesn't rationalise denominator. 3 marks also if gets right answer despite an error, by fudging it. 2 marks if multiple or major errors. 1 mark if starts off in right direction but loses it completely. Allow 4 if correct but k not stated. **[4 marks]**

13 (a)

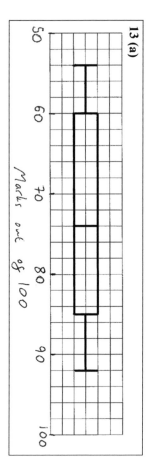

Marks out of 100

To draw a box plot (or 'box and whisker plot') you need to know the following things about your data:

• **The median:** Put the numbers in order from low to high, then take the middle number. If there are two middle numbers, go half way between them (find the mean), by adding them and dividing by 2.

• **The upper quartile (Q3):** Take the numbers to the right of (but not including) the median, and *find the median of these numbers.*

• **The lower quartile (Q1):** Take the numbers to the left of (but not including) the median, and *find the median of these numbers.*

• **The lowest number** and **the highest number.**

The upper and lower quartiles are **the ends of the box.**

The median is **the line inside the box.**

The highest and lowest values are **the 'whiskers'.**

Always label your axis! Just as with writing the correct units for an answer, this should become instinctive.

Marking: Subtract marks for missing elements in diagram and calculations. 0 marks if 3 errors. 0 marks if nice-looking diagram for entirely wrong values. Must have a scale for 3 marks, but permit missing axis label. 2 marks if scale planned inappropriately so chart space poorly used. **[3 marks]**

(b)   *Farieda was more consistent. Her results have a lower range.*

or

Farieda was more consistent. Her results have a lower interquartile range.

There would be no harm in mentioning both of these reasons (indeed, it would be a good idea, for the sake of security). However, the question only asks for one reason.

The important thing is not to be confused by the fact that Nicholas has a higher *median* score. He might do better than Farieda on average, but he is very inconsistent.

Marking: A mark each for correct answer and one of the reasons above. 0 marks if says Nicholas more consistent or if says Farieda but reason clearly shows no understanding so this was just luck. 1 mark if just says Farieda with no explanation. **[2 marks]**

14 (a)

$$(\sqrt{5} - \sqrt{4})(\sqrt{4} + \sqrt{5}) = (\sqrt{5} - 2)(2 + \sqrt{5})$$
$$= 2\sqrt{5} + 5 - 4 - 2\sqrt{5} = 1$$

Remember that when multiplying two brackets, $(A + B)(C + D) = AC + AD + BC + BD$. This was also discussed in **Paper 1, Question 13(b).**

Marking: 2 marks if minor error. 1 mark if multiple/major errors but right basic approach. **[3 marks]**

(b)

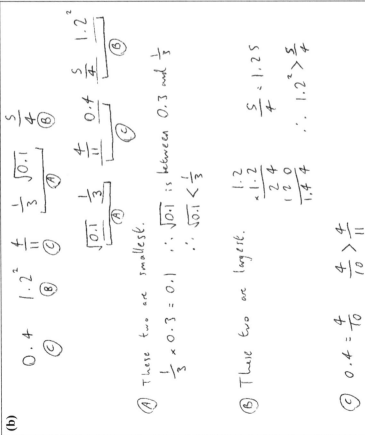

You may not need all the working shown above. For instance, it may be obvious that 1.2^2 is larger than $\frac{5}{4}$ and that 0.4 is larger than $\frac{4}{11}$.

Sometimes it is easiest to compare numbers by writing them all in the same form (as decimals or fractions). In this question, it is likely to be simpler to begin with obvious comparisons.

It is self-evident that some of these numbers are larger or smaller than certain others; the challenge is to compare very similar numbers, such as 0.3 and $\sqrt{0.1}$.

• Bear in mind that square-rooting a number greater than 0 and less than 1 *will result in a larger number*.

You could also deal with step **A** by considering that $\left(\frac{1}{3}\right)^2 = \frac{1}{9}$. This is larger than $\left(\sqrt{0.1}\right)^2$ or 0.1, which is $\frac{1}{10}$.

• If you have re-written some numbers in different forms (e.g. writing 0.4 as $\frac{4}{10}$), remember in your answer to *use the form given in the question.*

Marking: 1 mark if two numbers swapped/one number out of order (even if this has bumped other numbers up or down). If 2 errors in answer, inspect working for valid maths which can be rewarded with 1 mark. Permit correct answer with numbers in wrong form. **[2 marks]**

15 (a)

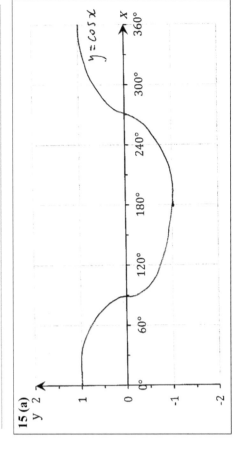

You need to be familiar with the graphs of $y = \cos x$, $y = \sin x$ and $y = \tan x$.

As you can see from the sketch above, your ability to draw an elegant curve is not overly important!

Your graph must clearly pass through (0 , 1), (90 , 0), (180 , -1), (270 , 0) and (360 , 1), and 1 and -1 must be its maximum and minimum values respectively.

Don't forget to label your graph!

Marking: 1 mark if essentially correct points but inaccurately drawn (e.g. cuts x axis at 100° rather than 90°). 1 mark if maximum and minimum points at y = 2. If graph does not have the correct overall shape (e.g. passes through (0 , 0)), then 0 marks. 0 marks also if several types of error. Lack of label on graph should be permitted. **[2 marks]**

(b) (i)

$$\text{Minimum is } y = \cos 180$$
$$\therefore \text{ If } y = \cos(x-35), \text{ min is when } x - 35 = 180 \quad \therefore x = 215°$$
$$(215, -1)$$

Another, more intuitive way of thinking about this problem is as follows:

- $y = \cos(x - 35)$ means that the value of y is *always based on something to the left* (a lower value of x than the one you are using at any given moment).
- Therefore the graph has been *pushed to the right* by 35°.
- Therefore the minimum value of y is not at $x = 180$, but at $x = 215$

This is a common kind of question at GCSE. It looks confusing, but the technique is simple to apply once you understand it.

Marking: 1 mark if $(145, -1)$ or $(215, 1)$. Otherwise 0 marks. No F.T. from **(a)** because simple cos values should be known. **[2 marks]**

(ii)

$$4 - \cos x \text{ is greatest when } x = 180 \quad \therefore -\cos 180 = -(-1) = 1$$
$$\therefore 4 - \cos 180 = 4 + 1 = 5 \qquad (180, 5)$$

- Because this equation involves a *negative* value of $\cos x$ (i.e. $-\cos x$), the graph has been flipped over (reflected in the x axis: $y = 0$).
- Because the equation includes $\cos x$, and not $\cos(x + 3)$ or $\cos 4x$ or anything of that sort, the maximum point (the minimum before the graph was flipped) *will still be at 180°*.

As $\cos 180 = -1$, it is clear that $4 - \cos 180 = 4 - (-1) = 5$

Marking: 1 mark if x value is 180 but y value is incorrect, or if y value is 5 but x is incorrect. **[2 marks]**

16   Method 1

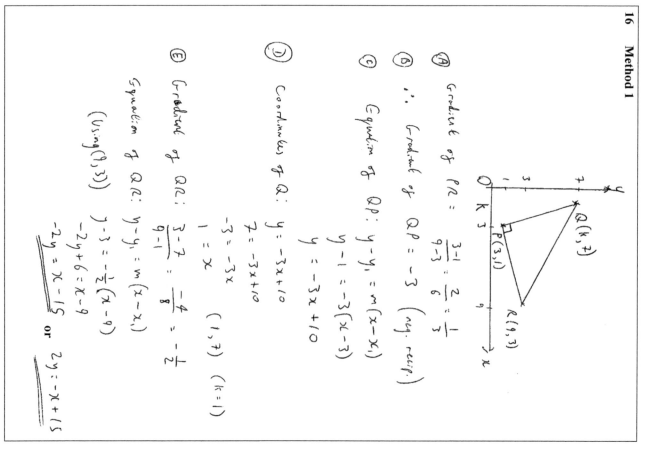

Ⓐ Gradient of $PR = \dfrac{3-1}{9-3} = \dfrac{2}{6} = \dfrac{1}{3}$

Ⓑ $\therefore$ Gradient of $QP = -3$ (neg. recip.)

Ⓒ Equation of QP: $y - y_1 = m(x - x_1)$
$$y - 1 = -3(x - 3)$$
$$y = -3x + 10$$

Ⓓ Coordinates of Q: $y = -3x + 10$
$$7 = -3x + 10$$
$$-3 = -3x$$
$$1 = x \qquad (1, 7) \quad (k = 1)$$

Ⓔ Gradient of QR: $\dfrac{3-7}{9-1} = \dfrac{-4}{8} = -\dfrac{1}{2}$

Equation of QR: $y - y_1 = m(x - x_1)$
$$y - 3 = -\tfrac{1}{2}(x - 9)$$
$$(\text{using } (9, 3))$$
$$-2y + 6 = x - 9$$
$$-2y = x - 15 \qquad \textbf{or} \qquad 2y = -x + 15$$

The first step should be to draw a sketch. Otherwise it would be easy to lose track of what you are doing.

Your first task is to find k, and therefore the coordinates of **Q**.

You can find this point if you know the equation of the line QP. This is set out in steps **A** to **D**.

A: Find the gradient of PR (see **Paper 1, Question 18(b)** for gradients).

B: The gradient of QP will be the **negative reciprocal** (**Paper 1, Question 5**) of your answer from step **A**, because the lines PR and QP are at right angles.

C: Use $y - y_1 = m(x - x_1)$ (**Paper 1, Question 18(b)**) to find the equation of QP.

D: Because we know that the y coordinate at **Q** is 7, we can use the equation of QP to find the x coordinate, k.

Now you need to find the gradient of QR. Using this and $y - y_1 = m(x - x_1)$, you can find the equation of the line!

Method 2

Instead of steps **A** to **D** above, you can use Pythagoras' theorem (**Paper 1, Question 3(a)**) to find k and the coordinates of **Q**. This alternative method is set out in steps **F** and **G** below.

This method is logical, but a little fiddlier than the one above.

(F) Length b of PR: $b^2 = 2^2 + 6^2$ $\therefore b^2 = 40$

Length c of QP: $c^2 = 6^2 + (k-3)^2 = 36 + k^2 - 6k + 9 = k^2 - 6k + 45$

Length a of QR: $a^2 = 4^2 + (k-9)^2 = 16 + k^2 - 18k + 81 = k^2 - 18k + 97$

(G) Combining using $a^2 + b^2 = c^2$:

$k^2 - 18k + 97 + 40 = k^2 - 6k + 45$

$\therefore 97 = 12k + 85$

$12 = 12k$

$1 = k$

Q is $(1, 7)$

F: Because getting from **P** to **R** involves going 2 units up and 6 units across, you can find the length PR *by imagining a right-angled triangle and using Pythagoras' theorem*. If we call the length PR b, then
$b = \sqrt{(2^2 + 6^2)} = \sqrt{40} \ldots$ but we are going to use Pythagoras' theorem again in step **G**, so it is better to leave the answer as $b^2 = 2^2 + 6^2 = 40$ (the reason for this will become clear later on).

- This is an important method, which you need to know, for finding the length of a line between two points on a coordinate grid.

Apply the same method to lines QP and QR.

- In these cases, your answers will be expressions involving k.

G: Now you need to *apply Pythagoras' theorem to the whole triangle*, PQR.

Using the values for a^2, b^2 and c^2 from step **F**, we can form the equation for a right-angled triangle, $a^2 = b^2 + c^2$ (where a is the hypotenuse: the longest side).

- This is sometimes given with the hypotenuse represented by c or h.

Solving this, you can find the value of k.

You now need to perform step **E** from **Method 1** in order to find the equation of QR.

> **Marking:** 3 marks if a correct method in outline, with significant errors. 2 marks for good signs of correct method but wrong turnings. 1 mark if there's something worth a tick! 4 marks for an almost correct answer. **[5 marks]**

17

Let x be the radius of circle A.

Area of A : πx^2

Area of B : $\pi(2x)^2 = 4\pi x^2$

Area of large circle: $\pi(3x)^2 = 9\pi x^2$

Shaded area : $\dfrac{9\pi x^2 - \pi x^2 - 4\pi x^2}{2} = \dfrac{4\pi x^2}{2} = 2\pi x^2$

$\dfrac{\text{Shaded area}}{\text{Large circle}} = \dfrac{2\pi x^2}{9\pi x^2} = \dfrac{2}{9}$

This is one of those satisfying questions where the working suggests that the answer will be complex, until a beautifully simple solution falls out at the end.

- You need to give a letter name to *the radius (or diameter) of* *one of the circles*, and then base all your working on this.

In the example, I use the radius of circle **A** and call it x; if you choose a different radius (of circle **B**, or of the large circle), your working will look slightly different, but the answer should be the same.

- The area of a circle with radius r is given by $area = \pi r^2$

The shaded area can be found by calculating

$$\frac{\textit{the area of the large circle} - (\textit{the area of } \boldsymbol{A} + \textit{the area of } \boldsymbol{B})}{2}$$

You reach your final answer by finding

$$\frac{\textit{the shaded area}}{\textit{the area of the large circle}}$$

and simplifying.

Marking: 3 marks if almost correct, but one or two minor errors e.g. with cancelling. 2 marks if a decent attempt at a correct method with big mistakes. 1 mark if attempts to find and compare areas but gets hopelessly lost while doing it. 2 marks if finds correct shaded area but forgets last step. **[4 marks]**

END OF PAPER 2 SOLUTIONS **TOTAL 80 MARKS**

For the exclusive use of the purchaser Not to be copied © Robert Lomax 2016

Paper 3 (80 marks)

If you wish to complete this paper in timed conditions, allow 1hr 30mins.

1　Write down the value of $(16x^2)^{\frac{1}{2}}$

.... **[2]**

2　The price of a pair of shoes has been reduced by 22%.

The new price is £33.15

Circle the calculation that will find the old price, before the reduction.

£33.15 × 1.22　£33.15 × 0.78　£33.15 ÷ 0.22　£33.15 ÷ 0.78

[1]

3　The nth term of a sequence is given by $n^2 - 3n + 2$

The nth term of another sequence is given by $5n - 4$

Find a positive number that is in both sequences and is less than 100.

.... **[3]**

4　The ratio of spoons to knives to forks in Rahim's cutlery drawer is 4 : 3 : 1

40% of his spoons are silver.

40% of his knives are silver.

0% of his forks are silver.

What percentage of his cutlery is <u>not</u> silver?

.... **[4]**

5　(a)　The point $(5, -4)$ is translated to point $(-2, 8)$.

This translation can be described by the vector $\binom{p}{q}$.

Write down the values of p and q.

$p = $ ....

$q = $ .... **[2]**

(b)   Vectors **a**, **b**, **c**, **d** and **e** are drawn on a grid:

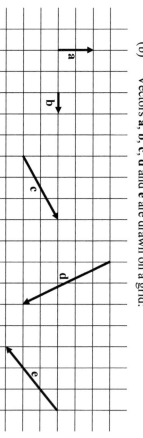

Express each of the vectors **c**, **d** and **e** in terms of **a** and **b**.

c = ...

d = ...

e = ...

[3]

6   (a) $f(x) = 2x^3 - x^2 + 3x - 9$

Find $f(-5x^2)$

Give your answer in its simplest form.

.... [2]

(b)   Fully factorise $96x^2 - 54$

.... [2]

(c)   Make y the subject of the following equation.

$$3y - 4 = \frac{5 - 3y}{2x}$$

.... [3]

8 **A** is the centre of a circle.

B, **C** and **D** are points on the circumference.

BC is a diameter.

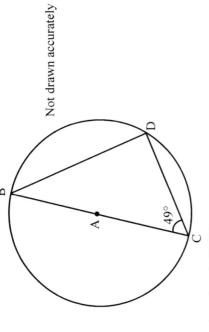

Not drawn accurately

What is the size of angle CBD?

.... **[3]**

9 Claire and Darren interviewed a number of football supporters from their school, asking each one which their favourite Premiership team was.

The following table shows their results:

Team	Frequency
Manchester United	9
Liverpool	5
Everton	4
Leicester City	17
Manchester City	12
Newcastle	1

---

7 ABCD is a trapezium. It has an area of 90cm².

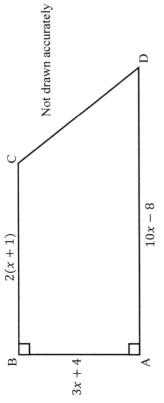

Not drawn accurately

Find the length in cm of AD.

.... **[5]**

Darren says that as there are 60,000,000 people in the United Kingdom who are old enough to support a football team, he can use his data to estimate the number of Manchester City supporters in the United Kingdom.

(a)   State two assumptions that Darren must make if he is to calculate an estimate based only on the information above.

[2]

(b)   Using the data above and accepting the assumptions in part (a), estimate the number of Manchester City supporters in the United Kingdom.

[2]

(c)   Claire does some research and finds that Darren's estimate is close to the true figure.

She says that he has just been lucky.

Do you agree? Explain your answer.

[2]

10   (a)   Complete the first numbers in the sequence $n^3 - n^2$ by filling in the empty boxes:

n	1	2	3	4	5	6
$n^3 - n^2$:	0					

[2]

(b)   (i)   Write down an expression for the sequence T, which begins like this:

-1   3   9   17   27   39

[2]

.... [2]

.... [4]

(ii)   1479 is the nth number in sequence T.

Find the value of n.

.... [4]

11   Niccoló has two identical, fair dice, **A** and **B**.

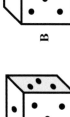

A   B

(a)   Niccoló throws **A** once.

What is the probability that he gets a prime number?

.... [2]

(b)   Now Niccoló throws <u>both</u> dice.

(i)   What is the probability that <u>only one</u> of the dice shows a prime number?

.... [3]

(ii)   What is the probability that the <u>sum</u> of the two dice is a <u>square</u> number?

.... [3]

12   (a)   Write down the exact value of sin 45°.

.... [1]

(b)   Find the area of the following triangle.

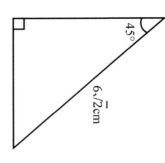

45°

6√2cm

.... [4]

13    $t \times 10^3 - t \times 10^6 = -2{,}997{,}000$

Find the value of $t \times 10^3 + t \times 10^6$

Give your answer in standard form.

.... [4]

14   The residents of Grosvenor Terrace include a number of people, all with two legs, and a number of dogs.

One of the dogs has three legs, and the others have four.

The total number of people and dogs is 151.

The total number of people's and dogs' legs is 355.

How many dogs live on Grosvenor Terrace?

.... [5]

16 (a) Find the turning point of the graph $y = x^2 + 8x + 19$

.... **[4]**

(b) Find the interval for which $x^2 + 11x + 24 \leq 0$

.... **[4]**

END　　**TOTAL FOR PAPER 3 IS 80 MARKS**

---

15 Here is a speed/time graph for an athlete running a complete race.

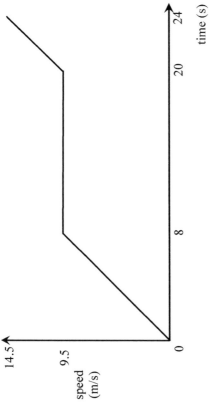

How long was the race?

.... **[4]**

Paper 3 – Solutions

1

Don't forget to square root 16 and x^2.

$$\left(16x^2\right)^{\frac{1}{2}} = \sqrt{16x^2} = \underline{\underline{4x}}$$

Marking: Correct answer only. [1 mark]

2

£33.15 × 1.22   £33.15 × 0.78   £33.15 ÷ 0.22 $\boxed{£33.15 ÷ 0.78}$

For a full explanation of why this is the case, see **Paper 2, Question 5(b)**.

Because the reduction in price involved finding 78% of the original figure (×0.78), you must reverse this using the reverse operation: **division**.

Marking: Correct answer only. [1 mark]

3

$S_n - 4$

∴ 4 less than 5× table

∴ every ...6 and ...1 number!

$n^2 - 3n + 2$ $7^2 - 21 + 2 = 30$

$0^2 - 0 + 2 = 2$ $8^2 - 24 + 2 = 42$

$1^2 - 3 + 2 = 0$ $9^2 - 27 + 2 = 56$

$2^2 - 6 + 2 = 0$ $10^2 - 30 + 2 = 72$

$3^2 - 9 + 2 = 2$ $11^2 - 33 + 2 = 90$

$4^2 - 12 + 2 = 6$ $12^2 - 36 + 2 = 110$

$5^2 - 15 + 2 = 12$

$6^2 - 18 + 2 = 20$

This question is easier than the working out above might suggest.

Firstly, because $5n - 4$ is a simple sequence, work out what it means:

• Every number ending in 1 or 6 is in the sequence, work out what it means.

Now you need to find numbers in the sequence $n^2 - 3n + 2$ which end in 1 or 6.

• If you work systematically, you can stop at $n = 4$, which gives a result of 6.

You don't necessarily need to write down your full working for each value of n up to that point. Use your common sense!

N.B. Some people might be tempted to try the following **wrong** method:

$$n^2 - 3n + 2 = 5n - 4$$

$$n^2 - 8n + 6 = 0$$

… and solve.

This gives values of n which are not whole numbers.

It does not work, because this method is looking for a point where the two expressions ($n^2 - 3n + 2$ and $5n - 4$) give the same result *and have the same value of n* (where they are at the same position in the sequence). This point does not exist (i.e. there is no integer solution for n).

Marking: 1 mark if some attempt to compare sequences. 2 marks if mostly correct but fails because of a calculation error. [3 marks]

5 (a)

$(5, -4)$ $(-2, 8)$ $\begin{pmatrix} -7 \\ 12 \end{pmatrix}$ $p = -7$
$q = 12$

$-2 - 5 = -7$ $8 - (-4) = 12$

Remember that vectors in a plane can be expressed as $\begin{pmatrix} x \\ y \end{pmatrix}$.

p is the x value, so you find this by subtracting the first x value (5) from the second (-2).

q is the y value, and requires the same process.

There are two common mistakes to avoid when forming column vectors:

- Do not subtract the wrong way round! This would give the reverse vector, from the second point back to the first.
  - In this case, you would **wrongly** get $\begin{pmatrix} 7 \\ -12 \end{pmatrix}$
  - (Use common sense: to get from 5 to -2 you must move *down*, and therefore in a *negative direction*.)
- *Even if your answer can be simplified,* **don't do it**! A vector is not a fraction! If you cancel the numbers in a vector, it will still point in the correct direction, but it will not take you far enough.
  - For example, $\begin{pmatrix} 2 \\ 1 \end{pmatrix}$ points in the same direction as $\begin{pmatrix} 6 \\ 3 \end{pmatrix}$, but it only goes a third of the distance.

Marking: 1 mark for $\begin{pmatrix} 7 \\ -12 \end{pmatrix}$ or $\begin{pmatrix} 12 \\ -7 \end{pmatrix}$. **[2 marks]**

4

s : k : F
4 : 3 : 1

(A) (x10) 40 : 30 : 10 (total 80)

(B) Silver: 16 12 0 (total 28)

(C) Not silver: 24 18 10 (total 52)

(B)   40   30
     ×0.4   ×0.4
     16.0   12.0

(D) $\frac{52}{80} = \frac{13}{20} = \frac{65}{100} = 65\%$

There is more than one way through this question, but they will all essentially be variants of the method above.

A: We do not need to know the actual number of each sort of cutlery, because we are only tasked with finding a percentage. We need numbers of spoons and forks from which we can easily find 40%.

- An easy way to do this is to multiply by 10 (you could also multiply by 5).

B: Find 40% of your new numbers of spoons and forks to establish the number which are silver ($\times 0.4$ or $\times \frac{4}{10}$ or $\div 10, \times 4$).

C: Find the number of each type of cutlery which is *not* silver.

D: Divide the total number of non-silver cutlery items by the overall total (which, if you multiplied by 10 at **A**, will be 80). Write your answer as a percentage.

Alternatively, you could skip step **C** by subtracting your result at **B** from 80; then use this result in step **D**.

- Whenever you are dealing with ratios / proportion, it is very useful to set out your numbers in columns, as in the example. You can make this easy by sketching a table for your figures before you start work.

Marking: 1 mark for some attempt to find percentages based on the given ratio. 2 or 3 marks for good working with major or minor errors respectively. **[4 marks]**

(b)

$$c = a + 3b$$
$$d = -2.5a + 2b \quad \text{or} \quad d = -\tfrac{5}{2}a + 2b$$
$$e = -1.5a - 3b$$

You could also write these the other way round (e.g. $c = 3b + a$), although alphabetical order is more conventional; or using fractions instead of decimals.

Remember to underline the letter name of each vector.

As in **(a)**, be very careful to point each vector in the correct direction (don't get the positive and negative signs jumbled), and don't mess with the magnitude of a vector in an attempt to 'simplify' it!

- $d = -2.5a + 2b$ **cannot** be written as $d = -5a + 4b$
- It *could* sometimes be written as $2d = -5a + 4b$, but not here: the question is asking for **d**, not 2**d**.

Marking: 1 mark for each. Correct answers only. **[3 marks]**

---

6 (a)

$$f(x) = 2x^3 - x^2 + 3x - 9$$
$$\therefore f(-5x^2) = 2(-5x^2)^3 - (-5x^2)^2 + 3(-5x^2) - 9$$
$$= 2(-125x^6) - (25x^4) - (15x^2) - 9$$
$$= -250x^6 - 25x^4 - 15x^2 - 9$$

Substitute $-5x^2$ for x, and be careful with the negative signs!

- $(-x)^2 = x^2$, but $(-x)^3 = -x^3$
- Also remember that $(x^y)^z = x^{yz}$

Marking: 1 mark if one or two minor errors. **[2 marks]**

(b)

$$96x^2 - 54 = 6(16x^2 - 9) = 6((4x + 3)(4x - 3))$$

This is fairly straightforward, so long as you don't forget the last stage! Look out for constructions like $16x^2 - 9$:

- Because both the numbers are perfect squares $((4x)^2 - (3)^2)$, and the sign is negative, you can factorise this into $(4x + 3)(4x - 3)$: **D.O.T.S: Difference Of Two Squares.**

- This is because, multiplying the brackets (working in reverse), the middle terms ($+12x$ and $-12x$) would cancel each other out, leaving $16x^2 - 9$.

Be aware that '*fully*' or '*completely* factorise' usually implies that there will be **more than one stage** in the solution. After each step, consider all the options again, until there is nothing left to do.

Marking: 1 mark if incomplete factorisation, or complete with a minor error. **[2 marks]**

(c)

$$3y - 4 = \frac{5 - 3y}{2x}$$

$2x(3y-4) = 5 - 3y$ ← Multiply both sides by $2x$ to remove the denominator.

$6xy - 8x = 5 - 3y$

$6xy + 3y = 5 + 8x$ ← Rearrange so that all the y terms are on the same side.

$y(6x + 3) = 5 + 8x$ ← Factorise to isolate y term.

$y = \dfrac{5 + 8x}{6x + 3}$

Your objective in a question of this sort is to remove any variables (x or y) from the denominators (lower halves) of any fractions, then rearrange until all the y terms are together. Then you must factorise for y, and divide to finish.

Marking: 1 mark if a reasonable attempt with major errors. 2 marks if minor errors. **[3 marks]**

7

$$\text{Area} = \left(\frac{\text{Top} + \text{Base}}{2}\right) \times \text{perpendicular height}$$

$90 = \dfrac{2(x+1) + (10x-8)}{2} \times (3x+4) = \dfrac{2x+2+10x-8}{2} \times (3x+4)$

$\qquad = \dfrac{12x-6}{2} \times (3x+4) = (6x-3)(3x+4) = 18x^2 + 24x - 9x - 12$

$\qquad = 18x^2 + 15x - 12$

$90 = 18x^2 + 15x - 12$

$\therefore \; 0 = 18x^2 + 15x - 102$

$\therefore \; 0 = 6x^2 + 5x - 34$

$\qquad = (3x \quad)(2x \quad)$ ✗

$\qquad = (6x + 17)(x - 2)$

$6x + 17 = 0 \; \therefore \; 6x = -17 \; \therefore \; x = -\dfrac{17}{6}$ (not volume because $-ve$) ✗

$x - 2 = 0 \; \therefore \; x = 2$

$AD: \; 10x - 8 = 10(2) - 8 = 20 - 8 = 12 \text{ cm}$

To find the length of AD, you first need to work out the value of x.

Because you are told the area of the trapezium, you can **form an equation, and solve it to find x.**

The area of a trapezium is given by $\frac{1}{2}(top + base) \times height$, and we know that this is equal to 90cm^2.

By multiplying and rearranging as above, you should arrive at the quadratic equation, $90 = 18x^2 + 15x - 12$. To solve a quadratic, you must first rearrange it to equal 0:

$$0 = 18x^2 + 15x - 102$$

You could solve this, but it will be much easier if you notice that it can be simplified, by *dividing every term by 3*:

$$0 = 6x^2 + 5x - 34$$

There are several things to consider when factorising this:

- $6x^2$ might be factorised into $3x$ and $2x$, or into $6x$ and x.
- -34 might be factorised into 17 and -2, or -17 and 2 (or 34 and -1 etc., but it is difficult to see how this might lead to a middle term of $5x$).
- $3x$ and $2x$ *look* more likely, and you can see that the example attempts to use them; but they **do not** work: a middle term of $5x$ does not result from them.

Some people find it easier to factorise like this:

$$6x^2 + 5x - 34 = 0$$

However, $6x$ and x **do** work, because $(-2) \times 6x + 17 \times x = -12x + 17x = 5x$, which is the correct middle term. (If you tried 2 and -17, you would get $-5x$, indicating that you only need to swap the signs.)

$$ax^2 + bx + c = 0 \quad (a \neq 0)$$

$$a \times c = 6 \times (-34) = -204$$

Now find **two factors of -204** which **add to give $+5$** (term b):

$$17 \text{ and } -12$$

Split the middle term using these numbers:

$$6x^2 + 17x - 12x - 34 = 0$$

$$(6x^2 + 17x) - (12x + 34) = 0$$

Factorise in two groups to get **a common bracketed factor**:

$$x(6x + 17) - 2(6x + 17) = 0$$

Therefore:

$$(6x + 17)(x - 2) = 0$$

Because AD has a length of $10x - 8$, it is easy to find that its length is 12cm.

- If you need to brush up on your quadratic equations, see **Paper 1, Question 13(c)**, which works through a less complex problem — then re-read the explanation here.

Alternatively, you might be able to solve this problem *using trial and error* with low values of x. Because $x = 2$, you would be likely to find the answer this way.

- However, this method is not recommended. What if x had equalled 44, for instance? You would have been at it for a long time!

A principle underlying this question is that **dimensions (lengths) must be at right angles in order for you to find area or volume** (unless you are using a trigonometric formula such as $A = \frac{1}{2}ab \sin C$ for a triangle, which is really a work-around for the same idea). This is the case for any 2D formula. Even in the case of a circle, πr^2 makes a square with side r then reproduces it 3.14... times.

Marking: 3 marks if finds x correctly but does not go on to find AD. Subtract a further mark for minor errors, and so forth. 4 marks if whole method but minor errors. 3 or 2 marks if whole method with multiple or major errors, respectively. 1 mark if some attempt at a correct method but with crippling errors. **[5 marks]**

8

$$CDB = 90° \quad (\text{angles of circumference in a semi-circle})$$

$$180 - 90 - 49 = 41°$$

This is easy if you know your circle theorems.

In this instance, you need to know that **angles in a semicircle are 90°**.

In other words, if you draw lines from opposite ends of a diameter to a single point on the circumference, the angle at the point where they meet must be 90°.

From the factorised equation, $0 = (6x + 17)(x - 2)$, x must be 2 or $-\frac{17}{6}$.

- Because the trapezium cannot have sides of negative length, only $x = 2$ is relevant.

You can prove this in the following way (the proof is worth learning, in case you need to reproduce it in an exam):

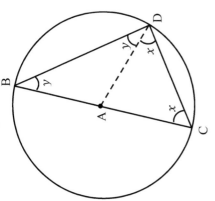

Angles ACD and ADC must be the same, because triangle ACD is isosceles (AC and AD are radiuses, so must be the same length).

For the same reason, angles ABD and ADB must be the same.

$x + x + y + y = 180°$, because these are the corners of triangle BCD.

Therefore:

$$2x + 2y = 180°$$

$$2(x + y) = 180°$$

$$x + y = 90°$$

($x + y$ is the angle at D [angle BDC], so this must be 90°.)

Marking: 2 marks if applies correct 'angles in a semicircle' rule but makes a mistake. 1 mark if recognises that angles in a triangle are 180° but not that BDC is 90° but not that angles in a triangle are 180°, or vice versa. **[3 marks]**

---

9 (a) *He must assume that his survey results are typical of football supporters in general* **[or *across the UK*]**.

He must assume that all people who are old enough support a football team.

You could also point out that he assumes younger people do not support football teams (although his phrase, 'old enough', does not tell us what age he is using as a cut-off), or that he assumes **48** people is a large enough *sample size* for a 60 million population.

Marking: Any two of the assumptions listed above. No mark for a point not clearly explained. **[2 marks]**

(b)

Total supporters interviewed : 48

$$\frac{12}{48} = \frac{1}{4}$$

$$\frac{1}{4} \times 60,000,000 = (5,000,000)$$

Do not complicate this by trying to avoid Darren's assumptions!

Marking: 1 mark if a single, minor error. No marks if just $\frac{1}{4}$ and no attempt to use this. **[2 marks]**

(c) *I agree, because Darren's assumptions are not supported by any evidence, yet would be likely to have a large effect on any calculation.*

You must agree with Claire here. Darren's assumptions were so unreasonable that his estimate is essentially a lucky guess. Any reference to the weaknesses mentioned for **(a)** above should be acceptable here.

Marking: 1 mark for agreement, and another for a reasonable explanation of why. Must do more than simply repeating Claire's assertion that Darren was lucky. **[2 marks]**

---

10 (a)

$n^3 - n^2$:	0	4	18	48	100	180

Marking: Lose a mark for each wrong number. **[2 marks]**

For the larger numbers, be prepared to check your calculations. It is dangerous to rely entirely on mental arithmetic, even if yours is good.

(b) (i)

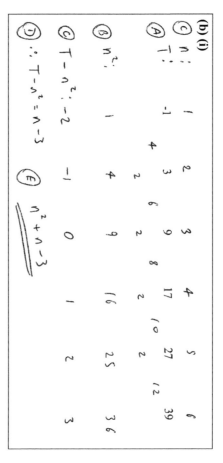

There is quite a lot going on here, but the steps are simple and logical:

A: Find the differences between the numbers in the sequences, and then find the differences between the differences.

- Because the numbers have a common second difference (of $+2$), the formula for the sequence must be quadratic.

It is useful to know the following rules for second differences:

- If the second difference is 2, your formula will be based on n^2.
- If the second difference is 4, your formula will be based on $2n^2$.
- If the second difference is 6, your formula will be based on $3n^2$.

… and so on.

Therefore, the formula in this case will be based on n^2.

B: Write out the first six terms of n^2.

C: Find the difference between the sequences T and n^2 (find $T - n^2$).

Compare $T - n^2$ with n.

D: Comparing $T - n^2$ with n, you can see that $T - n^2$ is the same as $n - 3$. Set these expressions as equal to each other ($T - n^2 = n - 3$).

E: Rearrange to get $T = n^2 + n - 3$: therefore an expression for the sequence T is $\mathbf{n^2 + n - 3}$.

Always check your final expression with the numbers in the original sequence, to ensure that you haven't made a mistake.

- For example, looking at the 4th term in the sequence, $4^2 + 4 - 3 = 16 + 4 - 3 = 17$, which is correct.

Marking: 3 marks for a minor error, or if gets to step **D** above but does not complete expression correctly. 2 marks for a decent outline of a method but some mistakes. 1 mark if finds correct second differences for T and recognises that sequence is quadratic, but the rest is wrong. **[4 marks]**

(ii) Method 1

$1479 = n^2 + n - 3$

$\therefore \quad 0 = n^2 + n - 1482$

1482

[factor tree: 1482 → ②, 741 → ③, 247 → ⑬, ⑲]

$\therefore \quad 1482 = 2 \times 3 \times 13 \times 19$

$= 2 \times 19 \times 3 \times 13$

$= \boxed{38 \times 39}$

$0 = (n + 39)(n - 38)$

$\underline{\underline{n = 38}}$

The first thing to say here is that 1479 is the nth number in the sequence … <u>We are **not** looking for the 1479th number! **Do not** try to find $1479^2 + 1479 - 3$.</u> (If you did this, your answer would be 2,188,917, and would involve a very large multiplication!)

- Instead, you need to solve $1479 = n^2 + n - 3$

So that you have a solvable quadratic, you must rearrange this to equal 0:

$$0 = n^2 + n - 1482$$

In order to solve this, we need to factorise it into the form $0 = (n + x)(n - y)$. Because the middle term of the quadratic is just n, it is evident that x and y must be consecutive numbers (they must be only 1 apart).

- Therefore we need to find two whole numbers which are consecutive and have a product of 1482.

This can be done by constructing a factor tree and finding prime factors.

- The prime factors of 1482 are 2, 3, 17 and 19
- $2 \times 3 \times 17 \times 19$ can be written as 38×39
- Because n is positive, $0 = (n + 39)(n - 38)$.

We can discount the result $n = -39$, because the sequence T begins at the 1st term and moves in a positive direction (see **(b)(i)**).

Therefore <u>**1479 is the 38th term**</u>.

Method 2

$1479 = n^2 + n - 3$

$\therefore \quad 0 = n^2 + n - 1482$

$\therefore \quad 0 = (n + x)(n - y)$

Where x and y are consecutive integers with a product of 1482.

$x = y + 1$

Trial and improvement:

$20 \times 21 = 420$

$50 \times 51 = 2550$

$30 \times 31 = 930$

$35 \times 36 = 1260$

$39 \times 40 = 1560$

$37 \times 38 = 1406$

$38 \times 39 = 1482$

$0 = (n + 39)(n - 38)$

$\underline{\underline{n = 38}}$

[multiplication workings:]

$35 \times 36 = 1260$

$37 \times 38 = 1406$

$38 \times 39 = 1482$

The method above is slower and less elegant, but it works fine, so long as you are careful with your calculations.

Method 3

$1479 = n^2 + n - 3$

$1482 = n^2 + n$

$1482 = n(n + 1)$

[**This shows that consecutive factors are needed.**]

Now solve by trial and improvement, as in Method 2.

11 (a)

Successes: 2, 3, 5

$$\frac{\text{Total successes}}{\text{Total actions}} = \frac{3}{6} = \frac{1}{2}$$

1 is not prime!

Don't forget to simplify.

(b) (i)

$$1 - (\text{Both} + \text{neither}) = 1 - \left(\frac{1}{2} \times \frac{1}{2} + \frac{1}{2} \times \frac{1}{2}\right) = \left(1 - \left(\frac{1}{4} + \frac{1}{4}\right)\right)$$

$$= \left(1 - \frac{1}{2} = \frac{1}{2}\right)$$

The best way into this problem is round the back, through the garden gate.

To find the probability that *only one* die shows a prime number, you should:

- find the probability that *both* dice show a prime ($\frac{1}{2} \times \frac{1}{2}$);
- find the probability that *neither* die shows a prime ($\frac{1}{2} \times \frac{1}{2}$);
- add these together;
- and subtract this from 1.

In other words, *by ruling out all the other possibilities*, you are left with the likelihood that only this event happens.

Any question which asks for the probability that **only** one thing happens is likely to suit a similar method.

Method 2 (sample space)

- Represent the numbers on each die along the axes of the chart.
- Tick the boxes which give the desired result (only one prime).
- Count the number of ticks (18) and divide by the total number of boxes (36).

$$6 \times 6 = 36$$
$$\frac{18}{36} = \frac{1}{2}$$

(ii)

The only possible square numbers are 4 and 9.

- Write out all the ways of making these numbers, remembering to count 2 + 2 only once.
- There are 7 possibilities, out of a total of 36 possible totals from 2 dice (because $6 \times 6 = 36$).

4: 1+3, 3+1, 2+2
9: 6+3, 5+4, 4+5, 3+6   } 7 options

$$6 \times 6 = 36$$

$$\frac{7}{36}$$

This gives a probability of $\frac{7}{36}$.

Method 2 (sample space)

	1	2	3	4	5	6
1	2	3	④	5	6	7
2	3	④	5	6	7	8
3	④	5	6	7	8	⑨
4	5	6	7	8	⑨	10
5	6	7	8	⑨	10	11
6	7	8	⑨	10	11	12

7/36

Here it is more useful to write the sum of the dice values in each square then circle the desired results (square numbers). Then proceed as in **(i)**, **Method 2.**

Marking: 1 mark if lists combinations but incompletely or with one or two errors. 2 marks if correct combinations but gets last stage wrong. **[3 marks]**

---

12 (a)

$$\frac{\sqrt{2}}{2}$$

For GCSE, you need to know the following values by heart:

θ	0°	30°	45°	60°	90°
$\sin\theta$	0	$\frac{1}{2}$	$\frac{\sqrt{2}}{2}$	$\frac{\sqrt{3}}{2}$	1
$\cos\theta$	1	$\frac{\sqrt{3}}{2}$	$\frac{\sqrt{2}}{2}$	$\frac{1}{2}$	0
$\tan\theta$	0	$\frac{\sqrt{3}}{3}$	1	$\sqrt{3}$	—

$(\tan 90° \text{ is undefined: as } \theta \to 90°, \tan\theta \to \pm\infty)$

The following triangles, used with **SOH – CAH – TOA** and Pythagoras' theorem, allow you to work out the values in the table:

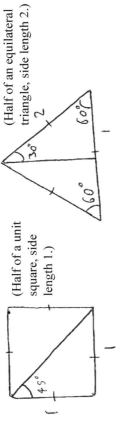

(Half of a unit square, side length 1.)

(Half of an equilateral triangle, side length 2.)

For example:

$$\tan 30° = \frac{opposite}{adjacent} = \frac{1}{\sqrt{(2^2-1^2)}} = \frac{1}{\sqrt{3}} = \frac{1}{\sqrt{3}} = \frac{\sqrt{3}}{\sqrt{3}} \times \frac{\sqrt{3}}{\sqrt{3}} = \frac{\sqrt{3}}{3}$$

It will probably be more efficient to memorise the results!

Marking: Correct answer only. $\frac{1}{\sqrt{2}}$ or equivalent is also acceptable. **[1 mark]**

(b) Here are three equally good (yet entirely different) methods for solving this problem. Only **Method 1** uses the answer to part **(a)**.

Method 1

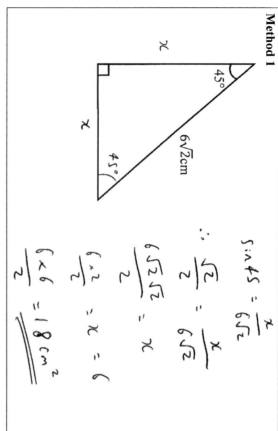

$$\sin 45 = \frac{x}{6\sqrt{2}}$$

$$\therefore \frac{\sqrt{2}}{2} = \frac{x}{6\sqrt{2}}$$

$$\frac{6\sqrt{2}\sqrt{2}}{2} = x$$

$$\frac{6\times 2}{2} = x = 6$$

$$\frac{6\times 6}{2} = 18\,cm^2$$

Because the triangle is right-angled and one angle is $45°$, the other must also be $45°$. Therefore the triangle is **isosceles**.

You need to know the following relationships:

$$\sin\theta = \frac{opposite}{hypotenuse} \qquad \cos\theta = \frac{adjacent}{hypotenuse} \qquad \tan\theta = \frac{opposite}{adjacent}$$

Many students use the mnemonic (memory aid) SOH – CAH – TOA.

- Using SOH ($\sin\theta = \frac{opposite}{hypotenuse}$), you can form an equation for x, replacing sin 45 with $\frac{\sqrt{2}}{2}$ from part **(a)**, and solve it to find that $x = 6$.

- Using the formula for a triangle, $Area = \frac{Base \times Perpendicular\ Height}{2}$, you can find the area, $18cm^2$.

Method 2

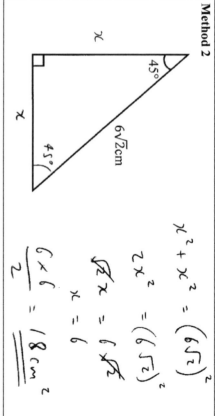

$$x^2 + x^2 = (6\sqrt{2})^2$$

$$2x^2 = (6\sqrt{2})^2$$

$$\sqrt{2}x = 6\sqrt{2}$$

$$x = 6$$

$$\frac{6\times 6}{2} = 18\,cm^2$$

This method uses Pythagoras' theorem ($a^2 + b^2 = h^2$), which has already been covered extensively in this pack.

Because the triangle is isosceles (see **Method 1**), you can form an equation for the length of the hypotenuse (longest side), and solve it to find x. As in **Method 1**, this can then be used to find the area of the triangle.

Method 3

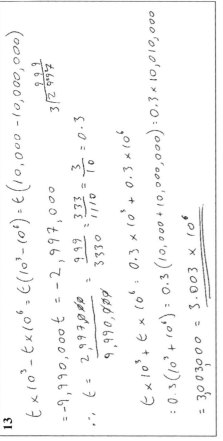

$$2\left(3\sqrt{2} \times \frac{3}{2}\sqrt{2}\right)$$

$$2\left(\frac{9}{2} \times 2\right) = \underline{\underline{18\,cm^2}}$$

This method is less obvious, but the working is (as you can see) quick.

I have made the triangle bigger so that you can see what is going on.

- As the triangle is right-angled and isosceles, it can be broken into two smaller right-angled isosceles triangles, with acute angles of 45° and side lengths of $3\sqrt{2}$.
- It is easy to find the area of one of these triangles and double it.

Marking: 1 mark if attempts correct method. 2 marks if minor errors. F.T. marks if correctly applies incorrect answer to **(a)**. **[3 marks]**

13

$$t \times 10^3 - t \times 10^6 = t(10^3 - 10^6) = t(10,000 - 10,000,000)$$
$$= -9,990,000\,t = -2,997,000$$
$$\therefore t = \frac{2,997,000}{9,990,000} = \frac{999}{3330} = \frac{333}{1110} = \frac{3}{10} = 0.3$$

$$3\overline{)2.997} = 0.999$$

$$t \times 10^3 + t \times 10^6 = 0.3 \times 10^3 + 0.3 \times 10^6$$
$$= 0.3(10^3 + 10^6) = 0.3(10,000 + 10,000,000) = 0.3 \times 10,010,000$$
$$= 3003000 = \underline{\underline{3.003 \times 10^6}}$$

The method is simple to understand, but the working out is a bit annoying.

As a starting point, bear in mind that <u>you are not told that the numbers in the question are in standard form</u>: t may not be between 1 and 10 … and indeed, it is not.

The most important thing to realise is this:

- You *cannot* <u>add or subtract different exponentials (powers) of the same number by playing tricks with the exponentials</u>, as you can when <u>multiplying or dividing</u>. You have to evaluate (find the values of) the numbers first, then add or subtract them.

It is important to <u>write your answer in standard form</u>:

- You must use 3.003, and <u>not</u> 30.03 or 0.3003

For a fuller discussion of standard form, see **Paper 2, Question 8.**

Marking: 3 marks if correct answer but not in standard form, or incorrect answer in standard form, spoilt by minor errors. 2 marks for multiple minor errors. 1 mark if correct approach initially but goes very wrong. **[4 marks]**

14

① Let the number of people = p and the number of 4-legged dogs = d

$$\left(\begin{array}{l} p + d = 150 \\ 2p + 4d = 355 - 3 = 352 \end{array}\right)$$

② ⓒ ① $\left(\begin{array}{l} 2p + 2d = 300 \\ 2p + 4d = 352 \end{array}\right)$

②-① $\quad 2d = 52$
$\qquad d = 26$

ⓓ $26 + 1 = \underline{\underline{27}}$

A: First of all, it is wise to remove the three-legged dog from your calculations. If you can find the number of four-legged dogs, you can then add 1 to your final answer. Otherwise, you will be creating equations involving three differently-legged creatures: people, four-legged dogs and three-legged dogs.

You will need to give letter names to *the number of people* and *the number of four-legged dogs*. p and d seem like sensible choices.

B: The number of people plus the number of four-legged dogs is 150 (151, minus the three-legged dog).

The number of legs on people and four-legged dogs is

$(2 \times$ *the number of people*$) + (4 \times$ *the number of four-legged dogs*$)$

and the total is 352 (355 minus the three-legged dog's three legs!).

C: Here I use the method of *elimination* to remove one variable. You could also use *substitution* (**Paper 1, Question 4**, and **Paper 2, Question 7(b)**).

I double all the values in the first equation, so that both equations include 2*p*.

I need to subtract one equation from the other, to remove the 2*p* term. Because the other terms in equation **2** are larger, it makes sense to subtract equation **1** from equation **2**.

This gives 2*d* = 52, which simplifies to *d* = 26 …

D: … But remember, 26 is the number of *four-legged* dogs. There is one more dog, with three legs, and it would be a shame to leave her out. She gets a hard enough time as it is. The total number should be **27**.

Marking: 4 marks if correct approach but minor errors. 3 marks if correct approach but multiple minor errors, or if gets in a tangle because doesn't treat the three-legged dog separately but otherwise a good try. 2 marks if some intelligent aspects but makes a mess. 1 mark if some evidence of understanding.
[5 marks]

15

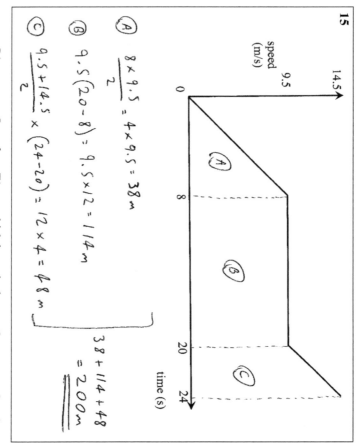

- *Distance* = *Speed* × *Time*, which is equivalent to **the area under the graph** of the athlete's speed.

To find the area under the graph, you need to divide it, as illustrated above, into a triangle (**A**), a rectangle (**B**), and a trapezium (**C**):

- Find the area of each of these shapes.
- Add them together.

The solution to **Paper 2, Question 3** contains a fuller discussion of the basic skills needed for speed/distance/time calculations.

Ⓐ $\dfrac{8 \times 9.5}{2} = 4 \times 9.5 = 38 \text{ m}$

Ⓑ $9.5(20-8) = 9.5 \times 12 = 114 \text{ m}$

Ⓒ $\dfrac{9.5 + 14.5}{2} \times (24 - 20) = 12 \times 4 = 48 \text{ m}$

$38 + 114 + 48$
$= \underline{\underline{200 \text{ m}}}$

Marking: 1 mark if attempts to use $D = ST$ but little understanding of how. 2 marks if major errors. 3 marks if correct method with minor errors. [4 marks]

16 (a)

(A) For $y = a(x+p)^2 + q$, t.p. is $(-p, q)$

$y = x^2 + 8x + 19$

(B) $= (x^2 + 8x) + 19$

(C) $= (x^2 + 8x + 16) + 19 - 16$

(D) $= (x + 4)^2 + 3$

(E) ∴ t.p. is $(-4, 3)$

This is an easily-neglected corner of the GCSE syllabus: **finding the turning point of a quadratic equation by completing the square.**

The **turning point** of a quadratic is the point *where the curve changes from a positive to a negative gradient, or vice versa*: the bottom of the trough, or the top of the hill.

For instance, the turning point of the graph on the right is here

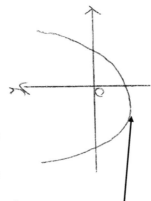

You need to memorise the rule given in step **A** above:

For $y = a(x + p)^2 + q$, the turning point is at $(-p, q)$.

So, looking at the question in front of us, we can see that we have to rearrange the equation $y = x^2 + 8x + 19$ into the form $y = (x + p)^2 + q$ (there won't be an a term, because the x^2 has a coefficient of 1).

This is the method known as <u>completing the square</u>. There are several ways of thinking about the process, but what follows is, in my opinion, the simplest one.

$$y = x^2 + 8x + 19$$

B: Put brackets around the x^2 and x terms, because these are what we will be focusing on:

$$y = (x^2 + 8x) + 19$$

C: Now we must complete the square:

- Take half of **8** (the coefficient of x), which is 4.
- Square it to make 16.
- Add this inside the brackets:

$$y = (x^2 + 8x + 16) + \cdots$$

We have done this to make an expression, inside the brackets, which can be factorised to give $(x + p)^2$.

- Also **subtract 16 outside the brackets,** so that the overall value of the right-hand side of the equation does not change:

$$y = (x^2 + 8x + 16) + 19 - 16$$

D: The expression in brackets factorises to $(x + 4)^2$, and the other numbers simplify to 3:

$$y = (x + 4)^2 + 3$$

E: Remember that **for $y = a(x + p)^2 + q$, the turning point is at $(-p, q)$**.

Therefore the turning point is at $(-4, 3)$.

Alternative Method: table of values

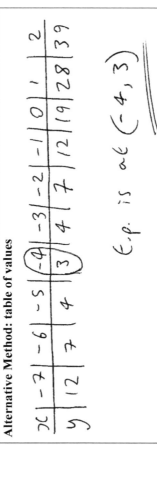

x	-7	-6	-5	-4	-3	-2	-1	0	1	2
y	12	7	4	3	4	7	12	19	28	39

t.p. is at $(-4, 3)$

I do not recommend this approach, because it leads to complexities when the coordinates are not whole numbers.

- Furthermore, **it is only useful for symmetrical graphs** such as quadratics.

However, it works here.

- From your sense of the graph, **choose an appropriate range** of x coordinates.
- Find the **corresponding y values**.
- Select the **lowest value of y** (or highest if the graph is 'upside down').
- Confirm that this is half way between the neighbouring values of x and y.

Marking: Completing the square: 1 or 2 marks for partial or good understanding, respectively, of method for completing the square, but major errors. 3 marks for good method with minor errors. Table of values or other method: 3 marks for clear understanding with minor error leading to slightly wrong solution. 2 marks for moderate or multiple errors. 1 mark for some understanding but a mess. **[4 marks]**

(b)

for $x^2 + 11x + 24 = 0$

$\therefore (x+8)(x+3) = 0$

$x + 8 = 0$
$x = -8$

$x + 3 = 0$
$x = -3$

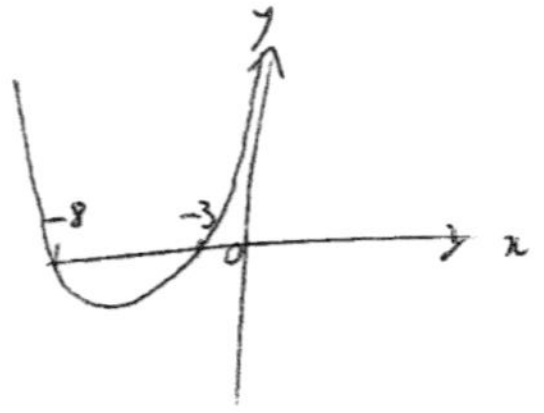

$\therefore x^2 + 11x + 24 \leq 0$ when $-8 \leq x \leq -3$

The sketch is useful, as a reminder that the graph is below the x axis where y is less than or equal to 0 (based on the positive coefficient of x, and so long as there are solutions).

In other words, you first need to solve the inequality *as an equation*, by finding the values where $x = 0$. You will then be able to express your results as an interval.

Factorising: Because all the values in the equation are positive, it will be easy to factorise so long as there are integer solutions.

- You need to find two numbers which multiply to give 24, and add to give 11.

The solution of quadratic equations by factorising is discussed more fully earlier in this pack: for example, see **Question 7 above** and **Paper 1, Question 13(c)**.

When you have the two values of x (-3 and -8) at which the graph crosses the axis, you can write an inequality to show the range (refer to your sketch at this point: because the x coefficient of the equation is +ve, there is one limited section of the graph below the axis):

$$-8 \leq x \leq -3$$

(A **table of values** could also work here, although it is likely to be slightly more time-consuming.)

Marking: 1 mark if attempts to factorise but rest is a disaster. 2 marks for good method but major/multiple errors, or if correctly finds x but does no more. 3 marks for minor errors, including incorrect use of inequalities based on correct values of x. Answer in words is acceptable: 'It is between $x = -8$ and $x = -3$' is worth 3 marks because does not specify whether these values are included, whereas '... between and including ...' is worth 4. Reward table of values or other method as in mark scheme for **(a)**. **[4 marks]**

END OF PAPER 3 SOLUTIONS   **TOTAL 80 MARKS**

Paper 4 (100 marks)

If you wish to complete this paper in timed conditions, allow 1hr 30mins.

1　This shape is a circle.

The lines cross at its centre.

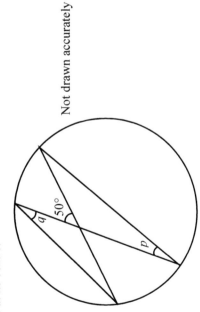

Not drawn accurately

Write down the values of p and q.

Give a reason for each of your answers.

p is ...... ° because..

....

....

q is ...... ° because..

....

....

.... **[4]**

2　(a)　Multiply $\frac{2}{3}$ by 4.68

Give your answer to 2 significant figures.

.... **[3]**

(b)　Divide 276.4 by 22

Give your answer to 2 decimal places.

.... **[2]**

3　Solve $-(x + 4) < 3 + x$

.... **[2]**

---

4 (a) Simplify $3^5 \div 3^{10}$

.... **[1]**

(b) Evaluate $8^{-\frac{1}{3}}$

.... **[2]**

(c) Evaluate $\left(\frac{64}{9}\right)^{-\frac{1}{2}}$

.... **[2]**

---

5 (a) Rewrite 2.75m^2 in cm^2.

.... **[2]**

(b) Rewrite 2.5km^3 in cm^3.

Give your answer in standard form.

.... **[3]**

---

6 Find the pressure exerted by a force of 5 newtons on an area of 40cm^2.

$Pressure = \frac{Force}{Area}$

Give your answer in *newtons/m²*.

.... **[3]**

---

7 Emma is choosing which ingredients to use in her biscuit factory.

- Caster sugar costs £0.60 per kg.
- Granulated sugar costs £0.50 per kg.
- Wheat bran flour costs £0.30 per kg.
- Plain flour costs £0.36 per kg.

In the biscuit factory, sugar and flour are mixed in the ratio 2 : 5

Emma is deciding between the following recipes:

Recipe A: Caster sugar and plain flour

Recipe B: Granulated sugar and wheat bran flour

How much more expensive is Recipe A than Recipe B?

Give your answer as a percentage.

.... **[4]**

For the exclusive use of the purchaser Not to be copied

8   ABC and EDC are triangles.

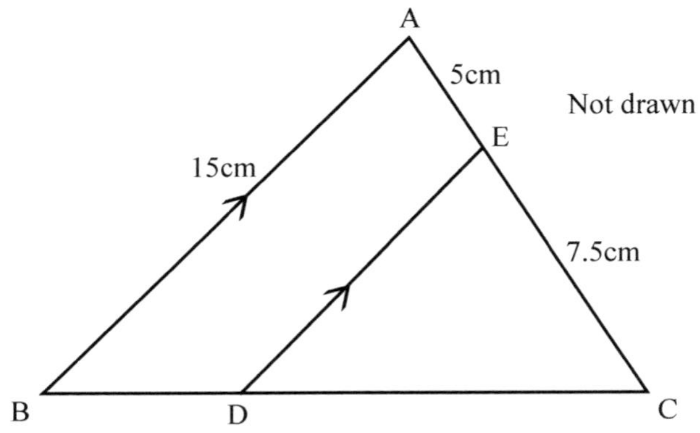

Not drawn accurately

(a)   Prove that triangle EDC is similar to triangle ABC.

[3]

(b)   Find the length of DE.

.... [2]

9   (a)   What is the resultant of $\binom{2}{3}$ and $\binom{1}{-5}$?

.... [1]

(b)   Given that $\boldsymbol{a} + \boldsymbol{b} = \binom{4}{-5}$, write the following as column vectors.

(i) $2\boldsymbol{a} + 2\boldsymbol{b}$

.... [1]

(ii) $\binom{10}{-2} - (\boldsymbol{a} + \boldsymbol{b})$

.... [1]

(iii) $3(\boldsymbol{b} + \boldsymbol{a})$

.... [2]

10   Between the years 1990 and 1995 inclusive, my height increased by 30%.

Between the years 1996 and 2000 inclusive, my height increased by 20%.

(a)   My father says that I was 50% taller in the year 2000 than I was in 1990.

Give a reason why my father is wrong.

(b)   What was the actual percentage increase in my height from 1990 to the year 2000?

.... [2]

.... [3]

11   This scatter graph shows the scores of 20 people in this maths paper, plotted against their ages.

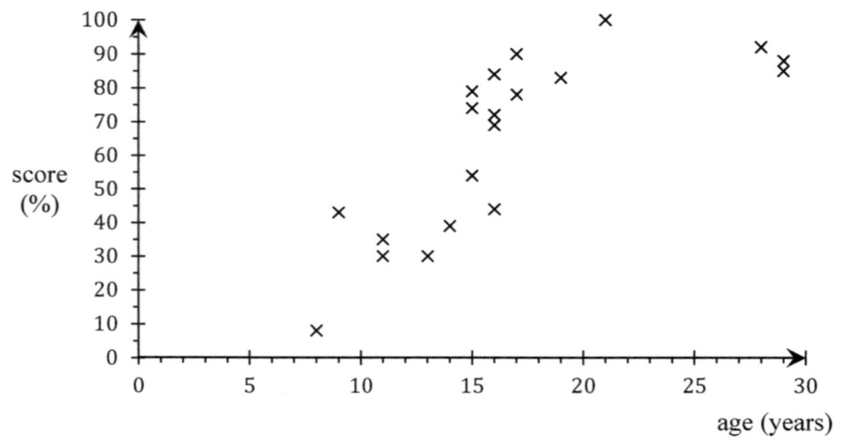

(a)   Use a line of best fit to estimate the score of a 25 year old.

.... [3]

(b)   What sort of correlation does the data show?

.... [1]

(c)   Pavel says that, according to the graph, a 21 year old is likely to score 100% in this maths paper.

Comment on Pavel's opinion.

.... [2]

12 You are given that

$$r = \frac{8p + 4}{p^2}$$

Show that $p = \frac{k}{r}(k \pm \overline{\sqrt{2k + r}})$ where k is a positive integer.

.... [5]

13 (a) Calculate $\frac{56}{9} \div 4\frac{2}{3}$.

Give your answer as an improper fraction in its lowest terms.

.... [3]

(b) Write $\frac{4}{15}$ as a recurring decimal.

.... [2]

(c) Write $0.0\overline{510}$ as a fraction in its lowest terms.

.... [4]

14 I have a box of blue, white and black sweets.

There are twice as many black sweets as white sweets.

I take a sweet from the box at random.

- The probability that it is blue is $\frac{1}{4}$.

I return the sweet to the box.

My sister then takes 12 white sweets and 12 black sweets from the box and eats them.

- The probability that I pick a blue sweet when choosing at random is now $\frac{1}{3}$.

How many sweets of each colour were originally in the box?

.... [5]

15 ABDE is a square.

BCD is a right-angled triangle.

The small circle has diameter x cm.

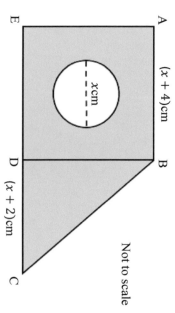

Not to scale

Show that the total shaded area is $\frac{1}{4}[(6 - \pi)x^2 + 44x + 80]$cm².

.... [5]

16 This is an octagon.

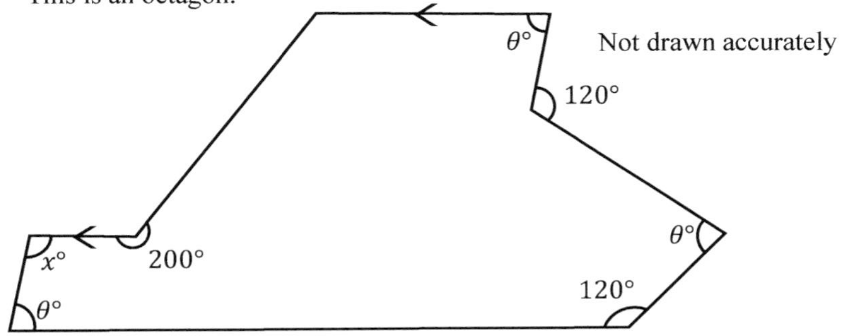

Not drawn accurately

Work out an expression for θ, giving your answer in terms of x.

.... [4]

17 On Bamburgh beach, the mass of a typical grain of sand is (6.98×10^{-4})g.

(a) Work out an estimate for the number of grains in 1,000kg of sand.

Give your answer in standard form to 2 significant figures.

.... [4]

(b) Cindy suggests rounding the mass of a grain to (5×10^{-4})g.

Would this be likely to produce an underestimate or an overestimate for the number of grains in 1,000kg?

Give a reason for your answer.

.... [2]

18   Shami, James and Roger are studying the graph of $y = 2x^2 - 20x + 32$

(a)   Shami says that it crosses the x axis at $(-8, 0)$ and $(-2, 0)$.

(b)   James says that it has a turning point at $(5, -18)$.

(c)   Roger says that it has a y-intercept at 16.

Determine whether each of them is correct.

You must show your working in each case.

(a)   <u>Shami</u>: crosses x axis at $(-8, 0)$ and $(-2, 0)$

.... [3]

(b)   <u>James</u>: turning point at $(5, -18)$

.... [3]

(c)   <u>Roger</u>: y-intercept at 16

.... [2]

---

19   (a)   Write down the gradient of a line which is perpendicular to the line

$$10y = 6 - \frac{4}{3}x$$

.... [2]

(b) A circle has a diameter of 5cm and centre **C**.

The line $6y = 95 - 8x$ is a tangent to the circle at point **P**
which has coordinates $(7, \frac{13}{2})$.

Find the coordinates of **C**.

.... [7]

END   **TOTAL FOR PAPER 4 IS 100 MARKS**

1

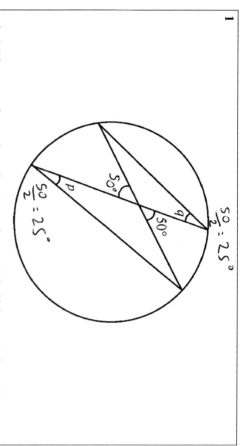

$\frac{50}{2} = 25°$

p

q

$50°$

$\frac{50}{2} = 25°$

p is 25° because the angle at the circumference is half the angle formed at the centre from the same two points.

q is 25° because the angle opposite 50° is also 50° and the angle at the circumference is half the angle formed at the centre from the same two points.

- *The angle subtended at the centre of a circle is double the size of the angle subtended at the edge from the same two points.*

- In other words, if you draw a line from two points on the circumference to the centre, then draw two lines *from the same two points* to a point somewhere on the circumference, the angle at the circumference will be half the angle at the centre.

- The angle opposite the 50° must also be 50°. Using the rule above, the angles at the circumference must all be 25° .

- Beware that the picture is very inaccurate: you have to trust the question, which states that the point of intersection lies at the centre of the circle.

Here is a proof for the rule above, showing a circle with lines meeting at the centre **C** (not labelled) and on the circumference.

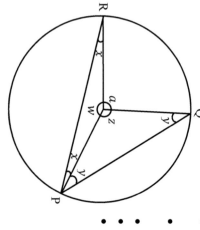

R

x

a

w

z

Q

y

x

y

P

- CP, CQ and CR are radiuses, so they must be equal.
- Therefore triangles CPQ and CPR are isosceles.
- $2x + w = 180°$ ∴ $w = 180° - 2x$
- $2y + z = 180°$ ∴ $z = 180° - 2y$
- $a + z + w = 360°$

Combining the above equations by substitution:

$$a + (180° - 2y) + (180° - 2x) = 360°$$

$$a + 360° - 2y - 2x = 360°$$

$$a = 2y + 2x$$

$$a = 2(y + x)$$

$$\therefore \text{Q}\hat{\text{C}}\text{R} \equiv 2 \times \text{Q}\hat{\text{P}}\text{R}$$

You could also solve the problem by realising that the angles at the centre must be 50°, 50°, 130° and 130° .

- On this basis, the other angles in each isosceles triangle must be $\frac{180° - 130°}{2} = 25°$

Marking: 1 mark for each answer, 1 mark for each explanation. Accept any wholly correct and reasonably clear explanation. **[4 marks]**

2 (a)

$$3\overline{)4.68} = 1.56 \qquad \text{or} \qquad 4.68 = \frac{468}{100} = \frac{117}{25}$$

$$1.56 \times 2 = 3.12$$

$$3.1$$

or

$$\frac{2}{3} = 0.6\overline{6}$$

$$\begin{array}{r} 4.68 \\ +\ 0.67 \\ \hline \end{array}$$

$$3.\ \frac{39}{1\,1\,7} \qquad \frac{78}{25}$$

$$\frac{2}{3_1} \times \frac{25}{1}$$

$$\begin{array}{r} 4.68 \\ \times\ 0.67 \\ \hline 3\ 2\ 7\ 6 \\ 2\ 8\ 0\ 8\ 0 \\ \hline 3.\ 1\ 3\ 5\ 6 \end{array} \quad 3.1 \qquad 25\overline{)78.00} \quad 3.12 \\ \,75.00 \\ \,3.00 \\ \,2.50 \\ \,.50$$

(Potentially less accurate unless you are confident with the effects of rounding.)

The first method is the simplest: find a third of 4.68, then double this to give $\frac{2}{3}$. Sensible rounding (as in the bottom-left method) is fine because the final answer only needs be given to 2 s.f. – but be careful!

- Always round your initial numbers (if you do this) to more significant figures / decimal places than are needed in the answer. The more leeway you allow, the less likely you will be to distort your result.

Remember: **Rounding to significant figures means counting from the first number which is not a 0** (but including any subsequent 0s).

Marking: 2 marks if a minor error. 1 mark if multiple errors, or a mess with some correct working. 2 marks if correct but not given to 2 s.f. **[3 marks]**

(b)

$$\frac{276.4}{22} = \frac{138.2}{11} = 12.563\ldots \qquad \text{or} \qquad 12.563\ldots$$

$$11\overline{)138.200}$$

$$12.56$$

$$11\overline{)138.200}$$

$$\begin{array}{r} 12.563\ldots \\ 11\overline{)138.200} \\ 110.000 \\ \hline 28\,200 \\ 22\,000 \\ \hline 6\,200 \\ 5\,500 \\ \hline 700 \\ 660 \\ \hline 40 \end{array} \qquad 12.56$$

Long division

Short division

As you can see, short division is considerably quicker for this problem.

There are two main ways in which you can set out long division (although the difference is mainly a matter of presentation):

- You can populate the spare working space with zeros (as here), or you can carry the numbers down without doing this (as in **Paper 1, Question 7**).

Marking: 1 mark if minor errors or correct answer not to 2 d.p. **[2 marks]**

3

$$-(x+4) < 3+x \qquad \text{or} \qquad -(x+4) < 3+x$$

$$-x-4 < 3+x \qquad\qquad -x-4 < 3+x$$

$$-4 < 3+2x \qquad\qquad -2x-4 < 3$$

$$-7 < 2x \qquad\qquad -2x < 7$$

$$-\frac{7}{2} < x \qquad\qquad x > -\frac{7}{2}$$

$$\text{(A)} \quad x > -\frac{7}{2}$$

You are probably quite comfortable with these questions by now.

Remember that (at step **A**), if you divide or multiply by a negative number, **you must reverse the inequality sign.**

Marking: 1 mark if minor errors but generally correct method. **[2 marks]**

---

4 (a)

$$3^5 \div 3^{10} = 3^{(5-10)} = \underline{3^{-5}} \text{ or } \underline{\frac{1}{3^5}}$$

For a reminder of the rules used here, and in parts (b) and (c) below, see **Paper 1, Question 10(a)(ii)**.

You could also write your answer as $\frac{1}{243}$ ($3^5 = 3 \times 3 \times 3 \times 3 \times 3 = 243$).

Marking: Correct answer only (any of the 3 options). **[1 mark]**

(b)

$$8^{-\frac{1}{3}} = \frac{1}{8^{\frac{1}{3}}} = \frac{1}{\sqrt[3]{8}} = \underline{\frac{1}{2}}$$

Evaluate means 'find the value of', so you should not leave your answer in index form.

In case the last step is unclear: $\sqrt[3]{8} = 2$ because $2^3 = 8$.

Marking: 1 mark if incomplete but correct. 0 marks if errors. **[2 marks]**

(c)

$$\left(\frac{64}{9}\right)^{-\frac{1}{2}} = \left(\frac{9}{64}\right)^{\frac{1}{2}} = \frac{\sqrt{9}}{\sqrt{64}} = \underline{\frac{3}{8}}$$

Remember that when a number is raised to a negative power (x^{-y}), you need to find its reciprocal: $x^{-y} = \frac{1}{x^y}$ and $\left(\frac{p}{q}\right)^{-y} = \left(\frac{q}{p}\right)^y$

Marking: 1 mark if gives $\left(\frac{9}{64}\right)^{\frac{1}{2}}$, $\sqrt{\frac{9}{64}}$, or equivalent, but errors after. **[2 marks]**

5 (a)

$$1 m^2 = 100cm \times 100cm = 10,000 cm^2$$
$$2.75 \times 10000 = \underline{27,500 cm^2}$$

First you need to find how many cm² are in a m².

It is then straightforward to multiply this by 2.75.

• **2.75 × 10⁴ cm²** would also be an acceptable answer.

Marking: 1 mark if gets 10,000cm³ but mistakes made afterwards. **[2 marks]**

(b)

$$1 km^3 = (100,000cm)^3 = (10^5 cm)^3 = 10^{15} cm^3$$
$$10^{15} \times 2.5 = \underline{2.5 \times 10^{15} cm^3}$$

or

$$1 km^3 = 100,000,000cm \times 100,000,000 cm \times 100,000,000 cm$$
$$= 1,000,000,000,000,000 cm^3$$
$$\text{Answer} \times 2.5 = 2,500,000,000,000,000 cm^3$$
$$= 2.5 \times 10^{15} cm^3$$

As you can see, the first solution (working with indices) is much tidier than the second (working with whole numbers).

If you need to revise standard form, see for example **Paper 2, Question 8**.

Marking: 2 marks if minor errors. 1 mark if some understanding. **[3 marks]**

6

A: Rewrite 40cm² in m², giving 0.004m².

B: Use the formula $Pressure = \frac{Force}{Area}$ with your answer from **A** and the given force of 5 newtons.

You could also find the answer in *newtons/cm²* and divide this by 10,000.

Marking: 1 mark if only one step is correct and the other very wrong. 2 marks if both steps understood but there is a mistake. **[3 marks]**

(A) $1 m^2 = 10,000 cm^2$ $\frac{40}{10,000} = 0.004 m^2$

(B) $P = \frac{F}{A} = \frac{5}{0.004} = \frac{5000}{4} = \underline{1250 \text{ newtons}/m^2}$

7

(a)

Recipe for 7kg (2+5): A: $0.6 \times 2 + 0.36 \times 5 = 1.2 + 1.8 = £3$

B: $0.5 \times 2 + 0.3 \times 5 = 1 + 1.5 = £2.5$

(b)

$3 - 2.5 = 0.5$ **(c)** $\frac{0.5}{2.5} \times 100 = \frac{5}{2.5} \times 100 = \frac{5}{25} \times 100 = \frac{1}{5} \times 100 = 20$

$\underline{20\%}$

A: A good starting point is to use the given information to find *a price for each recipe*.

- Because the given ratio is 2 : 5 and we have the price of each ingredient in £ per kg, it makes sense to find the cost of making **7kg of each mixture**; but you could make a different choice.

B: Find the difference between the prices.

C: Because we must find **how much more expensive Recipe A is**, we need to express the difference in price *as a fraction of the price of Recipe B*:

- $\frac{0.5}{2.5}$ equals $\frac{1}{5}$ or 20%.

Marking: 3 marks for a good method with minor errors. 2 marks if a good method with bigger mistakes. 1 mark if some understanding. **[4 marks]**

---

8 (a) To prove that the triangles are **similar**, you must **show** that that their angles **are the same** (*AAA similarity*).

BA and DE are parallel.

$\therefore$ BÂE = DÊC

AB̂D = ED̂C (corresponding angles)

AĈB is shared by both triangles.

All angles are shared by both triangles.

$\therefore$ ABC and EDC are similar.

This method proves that the angles are the same in both triangles. It is based on two facts:

- The angle at **C** (AĈB) is shared by both triangles.
- BA and DE are parallel.

Marking: 2 marks for a good understanding but a gap somewhere in the proof. 1 mark if some understanding but not proved. **[3 marks]**

(b)

Let DE = x

$5 + 7.5 = 12.5$

$\frac{7.5}{12.5} = \frac{x}{15}$ $\frac{7.5}{12.5} = \frac{75}{125} = \frac{3}{5}$

$\therefore \frac{3}{5} = \frac{x}{15}$

$\frac{3 \times 15}{5} = x = \frac{45}{5} = 9$

$\underline{9 \text{ cm}}$

If two triangles are similar, their sides are in the same proportion. DE will be in the same proportion to BA (15cm) as EC (7.5cm) is to AC (12.5cm):

$$\frac{7.5}{12.5} = \frac{x}{15}$$

Solve this to find x, the length of DE.

- This becomes easier if you rewrite $\frac{7.5}{12.5}$ as $\frac{3}{5}$.

Marking: 1 mark if very minor errors/ no units. **[2 marks]**

9 (a)

$$\binom{2}{3} + \binom{1}{-5} = \underline{\binom{3}{-2}}$$

The **resultant** of two vectors is what you get when you **add them together**: in other words, if you go 2 across and 3 up, then 1 across and 5 down (taking the

You can add vectors in any order.

Marking: Correct answer only. [1 mark]

(b) (i)

$$2\begin{pmatrix}4\\-5\end{pmatrix} = \begin{pmatrix}8\\-10\end{pmatrix}$$

This is because $2a + 2b = 2(a + b)$.

Marking: Correct answer only. [1 mark]

(ii)

$$\begin{pmatrix}10\\-2\end{pmatrix} - \begin{pmatrix}4\\-5\end{pmatrix} = \begin{pmatrix}6\\3\end{pmatrix}$$

Remember that $-(-5) = +5$.

Marking: Correct answer only. [1 mark]

(iii)

$$3\begin{pmatrix}b+a\end{pmatrix} = 3\begin{pmatrix}a+b\end{pmatrix} = 3\begin{pmatrix}4\\-5\end{pmatrix} = \begin{pmatrix}12\\-15\end{pmatrix}$$

As mentioned for (a), you can add vectors in any order: $3(b + a)$ is the same as $3(a + b)$ (**commutativity of addition**).

Marking: 1 mark if recognises $3(a + b)$. [2 marks]

10 (a) *He is wrong because the 20% increase includes 20% of the first (30%) increase, so it is more than 20% of the original amount.*

The question says that between 1996 and 2000, 'my height increased by 20% of my original height in 1990.

- In 1996 I was taller than in 1990, so 20% of *that* height is *more than* 20% of my 1990 height: I was more than 50% taller by the year 2000.

Marking: 1 mark if right idea but not clearly explained. [2 marks]

(b)

$$\begin{array}{r} 1.3 \\ \times\, 1.2 \\ \hline 2\ 6\ 0 \\ 1\ 3 \\ \hline 1.5\ 6 \end{array} \qquad 56\%$$

A 30% increase means finding 1.3 of an amount. A 20% increase means finding 1.2 of an amount.

Therefore, to find what a 20% increase of a 30% increase means overall, you need to find 1.2 of 1.3:

$$1.2 \times 1.3 = 1.56$$

An increase of 1.56 is a 56% increase (**not** a 156% increase, which would mean that I was more than $2\frac{1}{2}$ times as tall!).

Marking: 2 marks if 156%. 1 mark if right approach but errors. [3 marks]

11 (a)

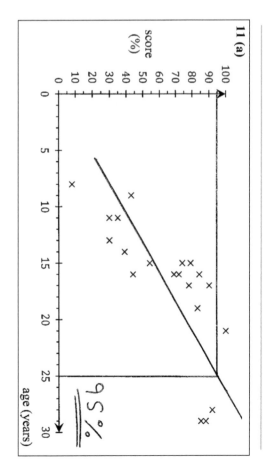

To draw a line of best fit, you should aim to leave the same (or a very similar) number of points above and below the line. The line should point in the direction which seems to best match the trend of the data.

- A line of best fit should <u>not</u> go through (0 , 0) unless there is a data point there. Even though it makes sense that a 0 year old would probably score 0%, this is a conjecture (a guess). *We have to focus on the evidence actually given by the data.* Your line should begin and end where the data does.

Similarly, this line of best fit implies that somebody older than 26 or 27 would score over 100%, which is impossible. This is one of the problems with this method.

When drawing lines from the axes to find a value (especially if the graph has no grid), it is helpful to use a set square if you have one, or another right-angled object: this way you can be sure that your lines are perpendicular. You could also use a protractor to help you.

Marking: Up to 2 marks for the line, depending how accurate. 1 mark if e.g. distorted to go through (29 , 80). 1 additional mark for an accurate reading from the line: permit accurate reading from incorrect line for this mark. **[3 marks]**

(b) *Positive correlation*

Positive correlation runs **up** from left to right; **negative correlation** runs **down** from left to right.

Broadly speaking, *if you can draw a line of best fit, there is correlation.*

For another discussion of this, see **Paper 1, Question 8.**

Marking: Correct answer only. **[1 mark]**

(c) *Pavel is wrong. Although one 21 year old scored 100%, the line of best fit shows that a 21 year old is more likely to score around 80%.*

The key phrase in the question is 'likely to'. This means that we have to think about what we might expect *another* 21 year old to score.

If you are picky (and well done if you are), you might say that the data would be better represented by a curve than a line: there is a clump of low data points roughly between the ages of 8 and 15, then a higher group (perhaps at the point

when people are revising for their GCSEs); the older group mostly seem to have got stuck at the GCSE level.

However, even if you were to use a curve, *the 21 year old's result would still probably lie above it ... but this is debatable.*

Therefore the following answers should also be acceptable:

> *Pavel is wrong, because the 21 year old's result is exceptional, and lies outside the main path of the data. The likely result for another 21 year old would be lower.*

or

> *Pavel is right, because the data forms a curve rather than a line, with age 21 at its highest point. A 21 year old is likely to score 100% or close to it.*

or

> *Pavel is right, because although the line of best fit does not clearly fit this data point, university students are likely to be confident with maths and might know all the answers. The graph goes down afterwards because people forget some maths.*

or

> *Pavel is right, because there should be one line of best fit for people still at school and university age, and another afterwards.*

If you say that Pavel is correct (which would be an unusual answer), you must explain your reason particularly clearly.

Marking: Any correct answer with convincing explanation. 1 mark if not fully explained but sense is clear. **[2 marks]**

12

(A) $r = \dfrac{8p+4}{p^2}$

$rp^2 = 8p+4$

$0 = -rp^2 + 8p + 4$

(B) $\therefore p = \dfrac{-b \pm \sqrt{(b^2-4ac)}}{2a}$ when $a = -r,\ b = 8,\ c = 4$

$= \dfrac{-8 \pm \sqrt{(64-[4 \times (-r) \times 4])}}{-2r}$

$= \dfrac{-8 \pm \sqrt{(64 + 16r)}}{-2r}$

(C) $= \dfrac{-8 \pm \sqrt{16(4+r)}}{-2r} = \dfrac{4}{r} \pm \dfrac{4\sqrt{4+r}}{-2r} = \dfrac{4}{r} \pm \dfrac{2\sqrt{4+r}}{r}$

(D) $= \dfrac{2}{r}\left(2 \pm \sqrt{4+r}\right)$ $(k = 2)$

If you are asked to rearrange a formula, it is important to have an idea (at least a vague outline) of what you are aiming for, so that you don't flounder around at random.

To help with this, there are a number of things to notice about the starting and ending points of this problem, as set out in the question:

• The starting equation contains p^2, so it is quadratic.

• The final equation does not contain p^2, and is in the form $p =$, so the *quadratic must have been at least partially solved* along the way.

• The final equation is in the form $p = r \pm \sqrt{t}$, which suggests that the **quadratic formula** $\left(p = \dfrac{-b \pm \sqrt{b^2-4ac}}{2a}\right)$ has been used.

Therefore it is likely that we need to rearrange the starting equation into the form $0 = ap^2 + bp + c$, then use the quadratic formula with a, b and c.

A: Multiply by p^2 *to remove the denominator.*

Rearrange into the '$0 =$' form needed for finding the roots of a quadratic.

B: Define a, b and c *and insert these into the quadratic formula stated* above.

C: Simplify further *by removing factors*. You can split the fraction into two halves (either side of the $\pm$ sign) or not, as you choose. The example does this.

Simplify.

Notice that $\dfrac{4}{r} \pm \dfrac{4\sqrt{4+r}}{-2r}$ is the same as $\dfrac{4}{r} \pm \dfrac{4\sqrt{4+r}}{2r}$ *because the $\pm$ symbol already includes both positive and negative options* (sometimes $\mp$ is used instead to show a change of sign).

D: Take out the common factor, $\frac{2}{r}$.

Now you need to check that your solution is in the exact form required by the question. If it isn't, you must first check that you can't simplify further or remove more factors. If you can't, you need to go through your working in search of mistakes.

Step C is the most likely stage for small errors to creep in.

Marking: 4 marks if correct method and reaches something close to required answer, but minor errors. 3 marks if good overall method but not close to answer. 2 or 1 marks for elements of good working. **[5 marks]**

13 (a)

$\dfrac{56}{9} \div 4\tfrac{2}{3} = \dfrac{56}{9} \div \dfrac{14}{3}$ (A) $= \dfrac{56^4}{9_3} \times \dfrac{3^1}{14_1} = \dfrac{4}{3}$ (B)

The question asks for an *improper fraction in its lowest terms*; in other words, a 'top-heavy' fraction which has been fully cancelled down.

A: $4\tfrac{2}{3}$ becomes $\frac{14}{3}$; see **Paper 2, Question 6** for a detailed explanation.

B: To divide fractions you must;

• flip the second fraction over;

• multiply.

Notice how the diagonal cancelling makes this problem much simpler.

• You can *only* **cancel diagonally** when you **multiply** fractions. You cannot do this when adding or subtracting.

Marking: 2 marks if very minor error or not fully simplified. 1 mark if correct method to divide but rest is hideous. **[3 marks]**

Marking: 3 marks for correct method but small error e.g. answer not fully simplified. 2 marks for right approach but e.g. tries to use 100x rather than 10x. 1 mark if vague idea of what to do but not really sure how. [**4 marks**]

14

Originally: (A) White:Black 1 : 2 ... and (B) if Blue is $\frac{1}{7}$, Blue : White : Black 1 : 1 : 2

(c) ∴ Blue $= \frac{W + Black}{3}$ and Black $= 2W$

After: (d) Blue $= \frac{(W-12) + (Black - 12)}{2}$

Substituting Black = 2W:

(E) Blue $= \frac{W + 2W}{3} = \frac{3W}{3} = W$

Blue $= \frac{(W-12) + (2W-12)}{2} = \frac{3W - 24}{2}$

(F) ∴ W = Blue $= \frac{3W - 24}{2}$ 2W = 3W - 24

$W = \frac{3W - 24}{2}$ ∴ W = 24

$W = \frac{3W - 24}{2}$ Blue = 24

(G) Blue = W ∴ Blue = 24

Black = 2W = 48   24 Blue, 24 White, 48 Black

(b)

0·266... or $15\overline{)4\cdot000}$ ∴ $\frac{4}{15} = 0\cdot2\dot{6}$

$$15\overline{)4\cdot000}$$
0·266...
3 000
×10 00
9 00
1 00

Divide the top by the bottom (the numerator by the denominator).

- Keep adding zeros after the decimal point under the 'bus shelter' until the recurring pattern is clear.

Marking: 1 mark for a minor error. [**2 marks**]

(c)

(A) Let x = 0·0510̇

(B) ∴ 10x = 0·510

(C) 10,000x = 510·510

(D) 10,000x − 10x = 510·510 − 0·510

∴ 9,990x = 510

(E) $x = \frac{510}{9990} = \frac{17}{333}$

This is one of the techniques that everybody studies and (almost) everybody forgets, at least the first time. Learn it! It comes up quite often in exams.

You are aiming to remove the recurring part of the decimal by subtraction.

A: Call the given number *x*, or any other letter.

Now we need two multiples of *x*: one which has the decimal point immediately before the recurring number, and one which has the decimal point immediately after it.

B: Multiply *x* so that **the decimal point** comes immediately **before** the first *set of recurring digits*. Here we need 10x.

C: Multiply *x* so that **the decimal point** comes immediately **after** the first set *of recurring digits*. Here we need 10,000x.

D: If you subtract your result in **B** from your result in **C**, you will have an equation in terms of *x* with no recurring decimals. Magic!

E: Solve the equation to give a fraction, and simplify.

There are various shortcuts you could take. For example, because my sister takes 12 each of two kinds of sweets, changing one tidy proportion (1 : 3) into another (1 : 2), it is probable that the original numbers were multiples of 12. This allows you to solve the problem using trial and improvement.

However, the method here gets you from beginning to end without guesswork.

Firstly, set up some ratios:

A: There are twice as many Black sweets as White sweets (2 : 1).

B: Blue sweets are a quarter of the total, so *there are three times as many other sweets as Blue sweets* (1 : 3). Because (2 : 1) adds up to a multiple of 3, the ratios are easily combined, so that the ratio of Blue : White : Black is 1 : 1 : 2

Now it is useful to form some simple equations:

C: Before my sister commits her great crime, *Blue sweets are a third of the total of White and Black sweets*. We also know that *there are twice as many Black sweets as White sweets*, so *Black = 2W* (be careful to get this the right way round).

D: After the theft, I have 12 fewer than my original number of White sweets and 12 fewer than my original number of Black sweets, and Blue sweets are half of this new Black and White total (because they are $\frac{1}{3}$ of the whole lot).

E: Because *Black = 2W*, we can replace *Black* with 2W in the other equations from C and D.

Simplify.

Now we can use these equations to solve the problem.

F: Because the right hand sides of the two equations each equal the number of Blue sweets, *they must also equal each other*: combine them.

Simplify and solve to find *W*, the original number of White sweets.

G: Use the original equations (or the ratio) to find *Blue* and *Black*, the original numbers of Blue and Black sweets.

Now check that your results work for the starting ratio, and for the situation after the raid.

15

(A) Square : $(x+4)^2 = x^2 + 8x + 16 = \frac{1}{4}(4x^2 + 32x + 64)$

Circle : $\pi\left(\frac{2x}{2}\right)^2 = \frac{\pi x^2}{4} = \frac{1}{4}(\pi x^2)$

(B) Triangle $= \frac{1}{2}(x+2)(x+4) = \frac{1}{4}(x^2+6x+8) = \frac{1}{4}(2x^2+12x+16)$

∴ Total shaded area $= \frac{1}{4}(4x^2+32x+64 + 2x^2+12x+16 - \pi x^2)$

$= \frac{1}{4}(6x^2 - \pi x^2 + 44x + 80)$

(C) $= \frac{1}{4}\left[(6-\pi)x^2 + 44x + 80\right]$ cm²

The total shaded area is the area of the square and the triangle, minus the area of the circle. In other words, the logic of this question is simple — but the algebra is a bit fiddly.

A: **The area of the square** is $(x + 4)^2$. Looking at the solution that we must find, it is evident that we will need to expand the brackets at some stage, and then take out a factor of $\frac{1}{4}$, so we might as well do this now.

• To take out a factor of $\frac{1}{4}$, we first need to multiply each term by 4.

The area of the circle is πr^2, and the radius here is $\frac{x}{2}$, giving $\frac{1}{4}(\pi x^2)$.

• This has a factor of $\frac{1}{4}$, so we don't need to play around with it.

The area of the triangle is *half the base × the perpendicular height*. The base is $x + 2$ and the height (from the square) is $x + 4$.

• Because the result has a factor of $\frac{1}{2}$, we need to multiply the terms inside the brackets by 2 in order to allow us a factor of $\frac{1}{4}$

B: Combine these to give the total shaded area (subtracting the area of the circle, of course).

Simplify by combining like terms.

C: Two terms ($6x^2$ and $-\pi x^2$) have a common factor of x^2, so this factor can be placed outside brackets.

You could skip the steps in **A** where we take out a factor of $\frac{1}{4}$, and do this later on, after combining the areas of the shapes. However, this would lead to some messier algebra, and therefore increase the risk of errors.

Marking: As for **Question 14. [5 marks]**

16

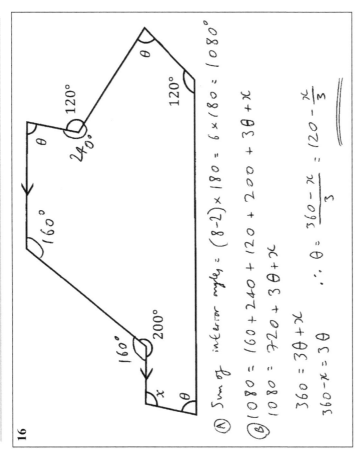

(A) Sum of interior angles $= (8-2) \times 180 = 6 \times 180 = 1080°$

(B) $1080 = 160 + 240 + 120 + 200 + 3\theta + x$

$1080 = 720 + 3\theta + x$

$360 = 3\theta + x$

$360 - x = 3\theta$ $\therefore \theta = \frac{360-x}{3} = 120 - \frac{x}{3}$

Notice the two 160° angles: they are *alternate angles between parallel lines.*

Be careful about the bottom left hand corner. It may **appear** that θ and x are between parallel lines, so should add up to 180°: however, there is no indication that the lines here really are parallel, because the line along the base *has no arrow.*

A: You need to find the total interior angle of an octagon. The total interior angle in degrees of any polygon is given by

$180 \times (number\ of\ sides - 2)$

This gives a result of 1080°.

B: Form an equation with your answer from A and the interior angles in the diagram, including θ and x.

Rearrange the equation to find an expression for θ.

Marking: 3 marks if a very minor error. 2 marks for multiple minor errors. 1 mark if major errors but overall approach understood. If does not know how to find total interior angles correctly but has good try at the rest, up to 2 marks. [4 marks]

17 (a)

(A) $6.98 \times 10^{-4} g = 6.98 \times 10^{-7} kg$

(B) $1000 kg = 1 \times 10^3 kg$

(C) $\frac{1 \times 10^3}{6.98 \times 10^{-7}} = \frac{1}{6.98} \times 10^{(3+7)} = \frac{1}{6.98} \times 10^{10}$

(D) $\frac{1}{6.98} \approx \frac{1}{7}$ $7 \overline{\smash{)}1.0^30^20}$ $= 0.142...$

(E) $0.142 \times 10^{10} = 1.4 \times 10^9$ (2 s.f.)

A: We need both figures (the mass of the grain and the total mass of sand) to be in g or kg, so it makes sense to sort this at the start.

- You could change either figure; I chose to change the mass of a grain into kg.

You change a mass in g into kg if you *divide* by 1,000, which means multiplying by 10^{-3}.

B: It is convenient to have both numbers in standard form.

C: *Total number of grains* $= \frac{Total\ mass}{Mass\ of\ 1\ grain}$

- Notice that $\frac{10^3}{10^{-7}} = 10^3 \times 10^7 = 10^{3+7} = 10^{10}$

D: We are only asked for an estimate, and 6.98 is extremely close to 7, so it is sensible to round it up.

$$\frac{1}{7} = 0.142\ldots$$

Marking: 3 marks if mostly correct but a minor error or two. 2 marks if e.g. good method but mixes g and kg, or rounds unwisely. 1 mark for some good ideas in a mess. **[4 marks]**

E: You must give your answer in standard form. See **Paper 2, Question 8.**

(b) *The answer is likely to be an overestimate, because the number of grains is given by* $\dfrac{Total\ mass}{Mass\ of\ 1\ grain}$ *so rounding the denominator down will give a larger result.*

Any explanation should be acceptable which explains that you will be dividing by a smaller amount than the true figure so will probably reach an overestimate.

I use the words 'likely' and 'probably' because the grain of sand is said to be 'typical', but we do not know what this means. We do not know that its mass is the *mean* mass of a grain.

Marking: 1 mark for 'overestimate'/'too high' etc. 1 mark for clear explanation. **[2 marks]**

---

18 (a)

$$y = 2x^2 - 20x + 32$$

When $y = 0$:

$$0 = 2x^2 - 20x + 32$$

($\div 2$) $\quad 0 = x^2 - 10x + 16 = (x-8)(x-2)$

$x - 8 = 0 \therefore x = 8$

$x - 2 = 0 \therefore x = 2$

$\therefore$ Crosses at $(2,0)$ and $(8,0)$

Shami is incorrect.

or

x-intercepts are when $y = 0$

When $x = -8$: $2x^2 - 20x + 32 = 2(-8)^2 - 20(-8) + 30$
$= 2 \times 64 - (-160) + 32 = 128 + 160 + 32 = 320$ ✗

When $x = -2$: $2(-2)^2 - 20(-2) + 32 = 8 + 40 + 32 = 80$ ✗

Neither equals 0, so Shami is incorrect.

You can either:

- Factorise to find the points where the graph crosses the x axis and compare these to Shami's coordinates. (See **Paper 1, Question 13(c).**)

- Substitute Shami's x coordinates into the equation and see whether her y coordinates are the result.

Marking: 2 marks available for working: 1 mark if minor errors or doesn't fully show how conclusion is reached. 1 additional mark for 'incorrect'/'wrong' as answer so long as answer is supported by working. **[3 marks]**

(c)

$$y\text{-intercept when } x = 0$$

$$y = 2x^2 - 20x + 32 = 2(0)^2 - 20(0) + 32 = 32$$

Roger is incorrect ___

The y axis is the line $x = 0$. Substituting this into the equation we find that $y = 32$ at this point: not 16. Therefore Roger is wrong.

Marking: 1 mark available for accurate working. 1 additional mark for 'incorrect'/'wrong' so long as supported by working. **[2 marks]**

---

19 (a)

$$10y = 6 - \frac{4}{3}x \qquad \therefore -\frac{1}{m} = \frac{15}{2}$$

$$y = \frac{6}{10} - \frac{4}{30}x$$

$$m = -\frac{4}{30} = -\frac{2}{15}$$

To find the gradient, we are interested in the coefficient of the x term when $y = mx + c$. However, this equation has $10y$ on the left hand side.

- Therefore we must *divide* $-\frac{4}{3}$ *by 10* to find the gradient, because the gradient m is found in the slope/intercept equation $y = mx + c$, **not** $10y = mx + c$.
- This gives us $-\frac{4}{30}$ or $-\frac{2}{15}$.

The question asks for the gradient of a **perpendicular** line, which means that we must find the **negative reciprocal**, $-\frac{1}{m}$, which is $\frac{15}{2}$.

Marking: 1 mark if $-\frac{15}{2}$ **[2 marks]**

(b) Method 1

$$y = 2x^2 - 20x + 32$$

$$= (2x^2 - 20x) + 32$$

$$= 2(x^2 - 10x) + 32$$

$$= 2(x^2 - 10x + 25) + 32 - 50$$

$$= 2(x - 5)^2 - 18$$

$$\therefore \text{ t.p. is at } (5, -18)$$

James is correct ___

<u>Complete the square</u> to find the turning point. (See **Paper 3, Question 16(a)** if you need to revise this method.)

- Notice that completing the square in this case involves **taking out a factor of 2** from the first and second terms.
- Therefore when you **add 25 inside the brackets**, you must **subtract 50 outside** so as not to change the magnitude of the right-hand side of the equation.

Method 2

x	2	3	4	5	6	7	8
y	0	-10	-16	-18	-16	-10	0

James is correct ___

A table of values works here, so long as you show clearly that this is the graph's axis of symmetry — i.e. that the y values to either side are symmetrical. For more about this method, see **Paper 3, Question 16(a).**

Marking: 2 marks available for working: 1 mark if minor errors or doesn't fully show how conclusion is reached. 1 additional mark for 'correct'/'right' so long as supported by working. **[3 marks]**

(b)

This is a fairly difficult question, so don't worry if you got lost somewhere along the way. Just be sure to learn from it, because there is some useful maths.

Before going through the following explanation, you might like to re-read the solution to **Paper 1 Question 18(b)**: I will take some of that knowledge for granted here.

First things first: **always sketch**. It makes a huge difference when you are trying to put your ideas in order, and will help you to avoid getting lost in your working. You don't need to be an excellent artist like me.

A/B: We are interested in CP, and would like to know its gradient. We know that a radius is perpendicular to the tangent which it meets on the circumference.

- Using the same technique as in part **(a)**, find the gradient of $6y = 95 - 8x$, then take its *negative reciprocal*: $\frac{3}{4}$.

Handwritten sketch and working:

$6y = 95 - 8x$

Ⓐ $\therefore m = -\frac{8}{6} = -\frac{4}{3}$

$-\frac{1}{m} = \frac{3}{4}$

$6y = 95 - 8x$ Ⓑ Gradient of CP is $\frac{3}{4}$

Ⓒ Gradient $\frac{3}{4}$

[triangle with sides 5, 3, 4] $3^2 + 4^2 = 25$ $\sqrt{25} = 5$

Ⓓ $\therefore$ CP is 2.5cm, not 5cm.

[triangle with sides 2.5, 1.5, 2] (dividing by 2)

Ⓔ $\therefore$ If P is $\left(7, \frac{13}{2}\right)$,

C is $\left(\left[7-2\right], \left[\frac{13}{2} - \frac{3}{2}\right]\right) = (5,5)$

Now we know the length of CP and its gradient. But how can we find the coordinates of **C?**

C: If the gradient of CP is $\frac{3}{4}$, the line must go up 3cm in the y direction for every 4cm it goes across in the x direction.

- Form a right-angled triangle showing these distances, then use **Pythagoras' theorem** ($a^2 + b^2 = h^2$) to find the *hypotenuse* (longest side) of the triangle, which runs in the same direction as CP.

- This gives 5cm.

D: But we know that CP is 2.5cm long, not 5cm!

- 2.5 is half of 5 … so if we find <u>half of each side of the triangle from step C</u>, we will know <u>how far to go down and how far across to travel from **P** to **C**</u>.

- 1.5cm down, and 2cm left.

E: Going 1.5cm down and 2cm left from **P** $\left(7, \frac{13}{2}\right)$, we reach $(5,5)$.

Therefore $(5,5)$ is the location of **C**.

Congratulations if you solved this correctly!

There are other possible ways of getting from step **C** to step **E**, but they are more complex and, at any rate, based on similar principles (Pythagoras' theorem/other Cartesian coordinate techniques). I won't make things unnecessarily complicated by suggesting more methods here.

Marking: 6 marks if a minor error or two. 5 marks if multiple minor errors. 4 marks if it gets gradient of CP and has a reasonable go at last step but gets stuck. 3 marks if errors throughout but several correct things and some sense of overall direction, or if correctly finds gradient of CP but no more. 2 marks if finds gradient of tangent but no more. 1 mark if attempts to find gradient of tangent.

[7 marks]

END OF PAPER 4 SOLUTIONS   **TOTAL 100 MARKS**

Paper 5 (100 marks)

If you wish to complete this paper in timed conditions, allow 1hr 30mins.

1   (a)   The length of a piece of string is 53.54cm, <u>rounded</u> to 4 significant figures.

Complete the error interval for the string's length.

.... ≤ length < .... **[2]**

(b)   The length of a <u>different</u> piece of string is 53.54cm, <u>truncated</u> to 4 significant figures.

Complete the error interval for the string's length.

.... ≤ length < .... **[2]**

2   (a)   Expand and simplify $(q - 4)(2q + 3)$

.... **[2]**

(b)   Factorise $36r^2 + 18r - 18$

.... **[3]**

3

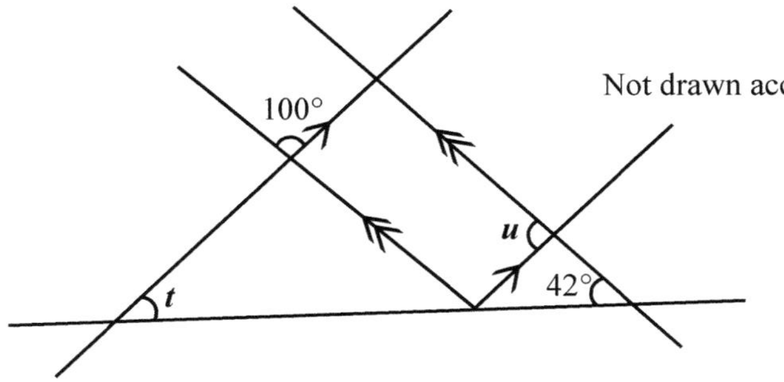

Not drawn accurately

Work out the sizes of angles *t* and *u*.

You must show your working.

t: .... **[2]**

u: .... **[2]**

4   (a)   Write 948 as a product of its prime factors.

.... [3]

(b)   What is the highest common factor of 948 and 620?

.... [3]

5   Bedazzle Bistro is serving ice cream sundaes, which contain vanilla ice cream, banana ice cream and chocolate wafers.

For a 480g sundae, they use 30g of chocolate wafers.

(a)   Find the value of **B** in the following ratio:

Vanilla ice cream, banana ice cream and wafers are served in the ratio 6 : B : 1

.... [2]

(b)   Bedazzle Bistro pays the following prices for each ingredient:

- Vanilla ice cream: £6 per kg
- Banana ice cream: £7 per kg
- Wafers: £5.50 per kg

If they sell 40 ice cream sundaes in a day for £4.20 each, how much profit do they make?

.... [4]

(c) £4.20 is a new price, after last week's price was reduced by 25%.

What was last week's price?

.... [2]

7 ξ, *S* and *F* are sets.

ξ = {*x*: 0 < *x* ≤ 100 *where x is an integer*}
S = {*square numbers*}
F = {*numbers which are not multiples of 5*}

(a) (i) List the members of the set *S* ∩ *F*.

.... [2]

(ii) Write down *n*(*S* ∩ *F*).

.... [1]

(b) Find *n*(*S* ∪ *F*).

.... [2]

6 Here is a triangle.

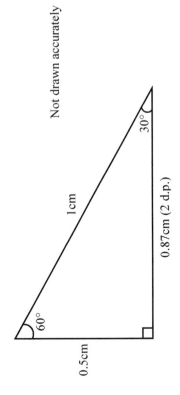

Not drawn accurately

0.87cm (2 d.p.)

(a) Circle the two statements below which are incorrect based on the values in the diagram.

cos 30° = 0.87   sin 30° = 2   tan 30° = $\frac{0.87}{0.5}$ cos 60° = 0.5

[2]

(b) What is the value of tan 60° to 1 decimal place?

.... [2]

8   On the following axes, shade the region where:

$$y > 2x + 1 \qquad 2y \geq 2 - x \qquad 3y \leq x + 12$$

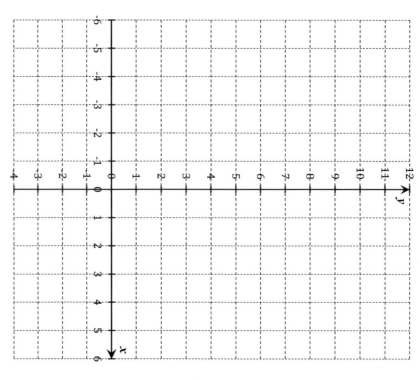

[5]

9   A bag contains 3 sweets and 2 stones.

Two items are selected at random from the bag and then returned.

The experiment is repeated 150 times.

Calculate an expectation for the number of times 2 sweets are removed from the bag.

.... [4]

10   Triangle ABC has area 120cm².

$$AB = \frac{\sqrt{3}}{2}BC$$

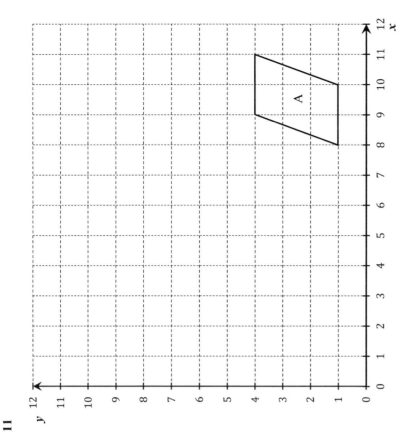

Not drawn accurately

Work out the length of BC.

Give your answer as a surd in its simplest form.

.... **[6]**

11

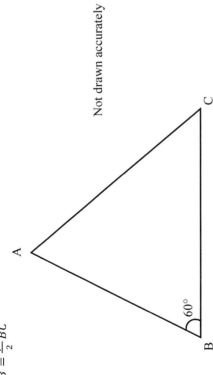

(a)   Enlarge shape **A** by scale factor −2, centre of enlargement (8 , 4).

Label your new shape **B**.

[3]

(b) (i) Shape **A** is enlarged by scale factor $\frac{2}{3}$ to make a new shape, **C**.

What is the area of shape **C**?

Give your answer to 2 decimal places.

.... **[3]**

(ii) Shape **A** is enlarged by a scale factor to make a new shape with area $10\frac{2}{3}$ cm².

What was the scale factor?

.... **[3]**

12   The following graph shows the displacement of a tennis ball during the 10 seconds after it is struck.

The ball travels into the wind. It blows backwards slightly before landing in thick grass.

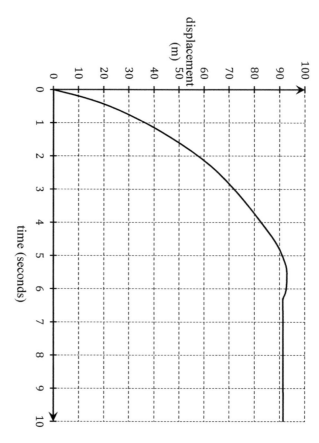

(a) (i)   After how long does the ball appear to strike the ground?

.... **[1]**

(ii) Describe the behaviour of the ball after striking the ground.

[2]

(iii) Describe the behaviour of the ball during the two seconds before it strikes the ground.

.... [2]

(b) By drawing an appropriate line on the graph, estimate the instantaneous velocity of the ball exactly 2 seconds after it is struck.

You must show your calculations.

.... [4]

13 $\tan \theta = \dfrac{2}{\sqrt{7}}$

Where θ is an acute angle, show that $\sqrt{11}\cos \theta = \sqrt{7}$

.... [4]

14 Sketch the graphs of the following equations, clearly labelling any points where they make contact with the x and y axes.

(a) (i) $-2y = 2x^2 - x - 15$

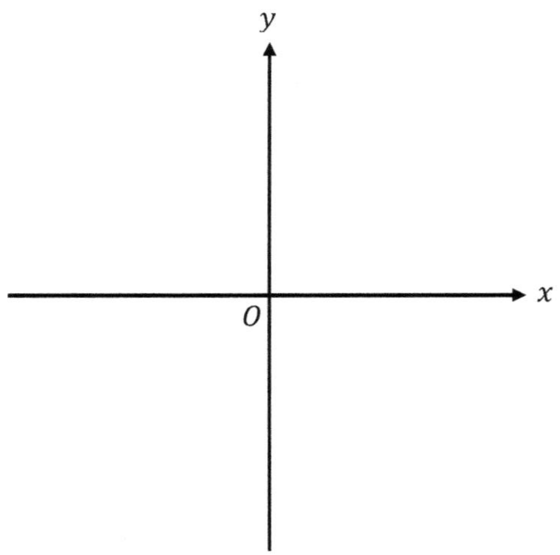

[3]

(ii) $y = -\dfrac{1}{x}$

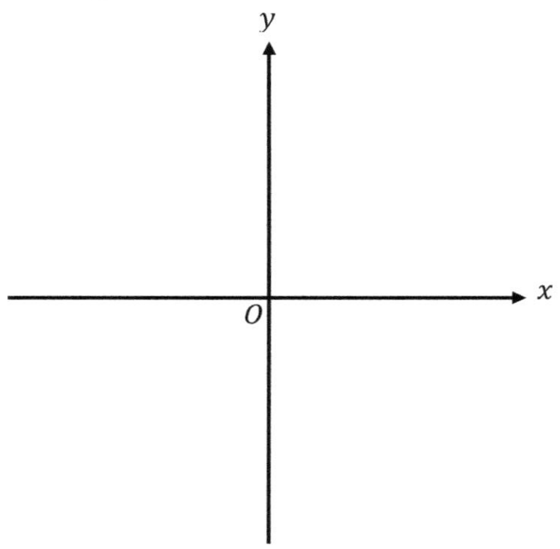

[3]

(iii) $y = x^3 - x$

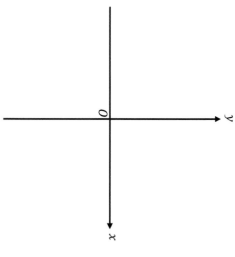

(b) Write down the coordinates of the two points where the graph of
$y = -\frac{1}{x}$ passes closest to the origin.

.... [3]

15 (a) Express $0.06\overline{44}$ as a fraction in its simplest form.

.... [2]

(b) Express $\frac{40}{333}$ as a recurring decimal.

.... [3]

16 (a) Find two points where the following graphs intersect.

Give your answers in the form (x, y).

$$5(x^2 + y^2) = 125$$

$$3y = 15 - x$$

.... [5]

(b)   Give a reason why there will be no other points of intersection
       for the graphs in (a).

[1]

17   p is inversely proportional to q.

When q is 6, p is 10.

Find the value of p when q is 9.

.... [4]

END   **TOTAL FOR PAPER 5 IS 100 MARKS**

Paper 5 – Solutions

1 (a)

$$53.535 \text{ cm} \leq \text{length} < 53.545 \text{ cm}$$

If the length of the string has been rounded to 4 significant figures, then it might have been rounded up or down.

- Any value from 53.535 (inclusive) would be rounded up to 53.54
- Any value up to (but not including) 53.545 would be rounded down to 53.54

You **DON'T** need to write the second number as 53.5449̇, or something of that sort, because the inequality signs given in the answer space give the 'inclusive' & 'but not including' used in the above bullet-points, without your needing to do anything else.

Remember that rounding to 4 s.f. means taking the first 4 digits in the number, *not including any zeros at the beginning.*

Marking: 1 mark for each value. **[2 marks]**

(b)

$$53.54 \text{ cm} \leq \text{length} < 53.55 \text{ cm}$$

'**Truncated**' means 'cut off'. In other words:

- Even if the length had been 53.54999999cm it would still have been written as 53.54cm, **NOT** rounded to 53.55.

Therefore the actual length of this piece of string must be a value equal to or above 53.54cm, and less than 53.55cm.

Marking: 1 mark for each value. **[2 marks]**

2 (a)

$$(q - 4)(2q + 3) = 2q^2 + 3q - 8q - 12$$
$$= 2q^2 - 5q - 12$$

Marking: 1 mark if a minor error e.g. a +/- sign incorrect. **[2 marks]**

By now you are probably familiar with this technique. See **Paper 1, Question 13 (b)** for a refresher if you need it.

- Be careful with the negative signs.

(b)

$$36r^2 + 18r - 18$$
$$= 18(2r^2 + r - 1)$$
$$= 18(2r - 1)(r + 1)$$

There are two stages here:

- Removing the common factor, 18.
- Factorising the quadratic.

You can revise this method by looking at **Paper 1, Question 13 (a)** and **(c)**.

Marking: 2 marks if a minor error. 1 mark if a couple of errors, or a bigger error but the right overall idea **[3 marks]**

3

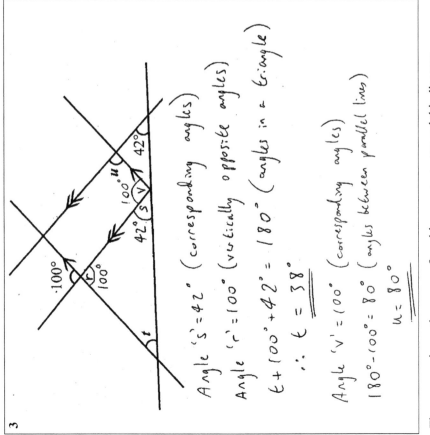

Angle 's' = 42° (corresponding angles)

Angle 'r' = 100° (vertically opposite angles)

$t + 100° + 42° = 180°$ (angles in a triangle)

∴ $t = 38°$

Angle 'v' = 100° (corresponding angles)

$180° - 100° = 80°$ (angles between parallel lines)

$u = 80°$

There are various other ways of working your way around this diagram.

Because the question indicates that your working will be marked, you need to make it very clear: essentially like a proof.

- Notice how the answer adds **labels to the diagram** and **linked explanations below** to show which rule is being used at each point.

This makes the reasoning completely clear.

Marking: 2 marks for each answer. 1 mark for each *wrong* answer if some correct geometric logic behind it. **[4 marks]**

4 (a)

948
3 · 316
   (2) · 158
      (2) · (79)

$948 = 2^2 \times 3 \times 79$

or

$948 = 2 \times 2 \times 3 \times 79$

Each number in the tree is split into two factors. Primes are circled, until the point where you find only primes: you can go no further.

- *If the question had asked you to write 948 as a product of **powers of its prime factors**, only the first solution would have been correct.*

Marking: 2 marks for a single, minor error. 1 mark for a reasonable attempt to find factors. **[3 marks]**

(b)

620
(2) · 310
   (2) · 155
      (5) · (31)

$948 = \underline{2^2} \times 3 \times 79$

$620 = \underline{2^2} \times 5 \times 31$

∴ HCF of 948 and 620: $2^2 = \underline{\underline{4}}$

Finding the highest common factor of several numbers is easy:

- List the factors of both (or all of) the numbers.
- Underline *all the factors they share*: here 2^2 is shared.
- **Multiplying** these factors (only one set of them – *don't combine the 2s from both lists*) gives the highest common factor.

Marking: 2 marks for minor errors. 1 mark for a reasonable attempt to find HCF. 0 marks just for factorising 620. **[3 marks]**

5 (a)

Firstly, the 1 in the ratio represents 30g of wafers in a 480g sundae.

- Because $\frac{30g}{480g} = \frac{1}{16}$, we know that the 1 is a 16th of the total amount, so all the parts of the ratio must add up to 16.

Therefore **B** must be 9.

$$\frac{3\emptyset}{48\emptyset} = \frac{1}{16} \qquad 16 - (1+6) = \underline{\underline{9}}$$

Marking: 1 mark for essentially correct method with minor mistake. **[2 marks]**

(b)

	V	:	B	:	W
(A) (×30)	6	:	9	:	1
(B)	(180g)	:	270g	:	30g
(C) (×40)	7.2kg	:	10.8kg	:	1.2kg

(D) Cost of ingredients: $7.2 \times 6 + 10.8 \times 7 + 5.5 \times 1.2$
$= 43.2 + 75.6 + 6.6 = £125.40$

(E) Revenue: $4.2 \times 40 = £168$

(F) Profit: $168 - 125.4 = £42.60$

To find the profit, based on the information we have, we need to subtract the cost of the ingredients from the money made (revenue).

A: Set out the ratio from part **(a)**.

B: Because one unit represents 30g, we need to **multiply each column by 30** to find the mass of each ingredient.

C: We are dealing with 40 ice creams, so it makes sense to **multiply by 40** at this stage. (This could also be done later in the working.) I have left out the column multiplications which would probably be necessary here.

D: Multiply the masses from **C** by the costs listed in the question to find **the total cost of ingredients.**

E: Find the **total revenue** (income) by multiplying £4.20 by 40 ice creams.

F: **Subtract the total cost from the total revenue** to find the profit.

Marking: 3 marks for overall method with minor errors. 2 marks if part of the working correct but another missing, or if overall method but larger errors. 1 mark if something deserves credit. **[4 marks]**

(c)

$$\xrightarrow{\times 0.75} \quad \xleftarrow{\div 0.75}$$

$$\frac{4.2}{0.75} = \frac{420}{75} = \frac{84}{15} = \frac{28}{5} = \underline{\underline{£5.60}}$$

The diagram on the left is a reminder that:

- If the price has been reduced by 25%, this means that it was **multiplied by 0.75** (i.e. it is 75% of the old price).
- To reverse this, you must **divide by 0.75**.

Marking: 1 mark if correct concept but a calculation error. **[2 marks]**

6 (a)

$$\cos 30° = 0.87$$

$$\boxed{\sin 30° = 2} \qquad \boxed{\tan 30° = \frac{0.87}{0.5}} \qquad \cos 60° = 0.5$$

$\cos 30° = \frac{adjacent}{hypotenuse} = \frac{0.87}{1} = 0.87$ **(correct)**

$\sin 30° = \frac{opposite}{hypotenuse} = \frac{0.5}{1} = 0.5$ **(not 2, so incorrect)**

$\tan 30° = \frac{opposite}{adjacent} = \frac{0.5}{0.87}$ **(not $\frac{0.87}{0.5}$ so incorrect)**

$\cos 60° = \frac{adjacent}{hypotenuse} = \frac{0.5}{1} = 0.5$ **(correct)**

Marking: 1 mark for each correctly circled answer. 0 marks if more than two answers circled. **[2 marks]**

(b)

(TOA)

$$\tan 60° = \frac{0.87}{0.5} = \frac{1.74}{1} = 1.7 \ (1 \text{ d.p.})$$

It's useful to note down the relevant rule as a reminder:

- **TOA** is a *mnemonic* (memory aid) for **tan θ** $= \frac{opposite}{adjacent}$ (where the **adjacent** length is the side next to θ, which is not a hypotenuse).

Notice the second step here: rather than dividing 0.87 by 0.5, which would be fiddly, you can *double the top and bottom of the fraction* (because 0.5 × 2 = 1).

Marking: 1 mark if a decent attempt to apply TOA but calculation errors. **[2 marks]**

7 (a) (i)

1, 4, 9, 16, 36, 49, 64, 81

First, some terminology:

- **Sets** are simply groups of items – in this case, numbers.
- ξ is the Greek letter *epsilon*, which is used to mean **the universal set**: all the items relevant to the question.
- S ∩ F means the **intersection** of sets S and F: all the numbers which are in **both** sets.
  - You can remember this by imaging ∩ as an upside-down bowl overlapping the edges of two trays: *it covers some of both of them, but not all of their contents.*

The intersection of S and F is all the numbers which are square and which are not multiples of 5. The universal set limits us to numbers between 0 and 100.

Marking: 1 mark if one number missing OR if one number present which is in one set but not both. 0 marks if multiple errors, or if a number is present which is from neither set. **[2 marks]**

(ii)

8

- n(S ∩ F) means **the number of items in S ∩ F**.

You simply need to count the numbers in your answer to **(i)**!

Marking: Correct count of the numbers in **(i)** (f.t. marking). An answer of 8 which is not the correct count of the numbers in **(i)** is 0 marks, because presumably is a lucky guess/coincidence (unless **(i)** was left unanswered, in which case 8 is correct, or unless new working is provided here). **[1 mark]**

(b)

$$n(S \cup F) = 100 - [\text{ multiples of } S \text{ which are not square }]$$
$$= 100 - 18 = 82$$

S ∪ F means the **union** of sets S and F.

- This means you must combine the sets: S ∪ F contains <u>all the numbers</u> which appear in either set.
- n(S ∪ F) means the number of items in S ∪ F.

You could find the number of items in S and the number of items in F, then subtract the number of items which are in both (to avoid duplicate entries – e.g. 16 is in both sets). This would take a while.

Because we know that there are 100 items in the universal set ξ, it is much faster to subtract from 100 the number of items which are in **neither** set.

Marking: 1 mark for a correct method with an error, e.g. miscounting 'multiples of 5 which are not square'. **[2 marks]**

8

$y = 2x + 1$

$2 \times 5 \times 1 = 11$

(when $x = 5$)

$2y = 2 - x$

$y = -\dfrac{3}{2}$

(when $x = 5$)

$3y = x + 12$

$3y = 3 + 12 < 15$

$y = 5$

(when $x = 3$)

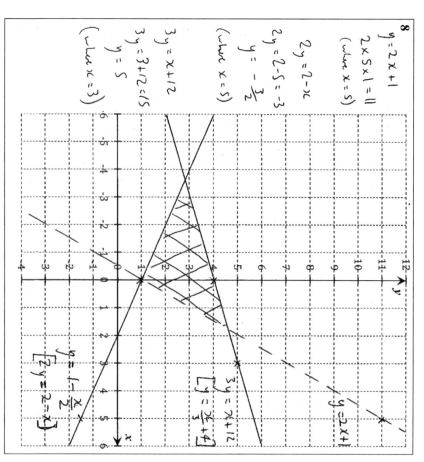

$y = -1 - \dfrac{x}{2}$

$[2y = 2 - x]$

$3y = x + 12$

$\left[y = \dfrac{x}{3} + 4 \right]$

$y = 2x + 1$

Before you begin drawing lines to represent the inequalities, it is important to remember this rule:

- Where the inequality sign is ≤ or ≥ the line must be **solid** to show that *values on the line are included.*

- Where the inequality sign is < or >, the line must be **dashed** to show that *values on the line are not included.*

In order to represent the inequalities as lines, it is convenient first to re-write them as equations (with an =).

You are probably comfortable with the method for representing equations as lines, but here is a reminder:

- You need two points on each line. Check the line with a third.

- Where an equation is in the form $y = mx + c$, c is the y value where the line crosses the y axis. Therefore two of the lines cross at $(0, 1)$ ($2y = 2 - x$ can be rewritten as $y = -\frac{1}{2}x + 1$), and the other crosses at $(0, 4)$.

- You need to find another point on the line, a reasonable distance from the y axis (because if the points are too close together, it will be difficult to draw the line accurately).

- This can be found *by putting a suitable value of x into the equation*. It is best to find a point where both x and y are integers (whole numbers), if possible.

- Another method is to use m, the gradient: For example, with a gradient of 2, you can go 2 squares in the x direction and 1 square in the y direction to find the next integer point on the line.

Notice that **the lines are labelled as equations, not inequalities.** This is because the inequality is not the line itself, but the region to one side of it.

- Don't forget to **label your lines and shade the region that satisfies all the conditions.**

- **If y is *less than* a function of x** ($y < \cdots$ or $y \leq \cdots$), then **the shaded space will be below the line,** and vice versa.

Marking: Deduct a mark for each minor error: e.g. doesn't distinguish between dotted and solid lines, or mixes these up; or a point in a slightly wrong place. Deduct 2 marks for each major error. However, allow up to 2 marks for a decent overall understanding when answer is a mess. **[5 marks]**

9

Where Sweets are W and Stones are T :

Second pick

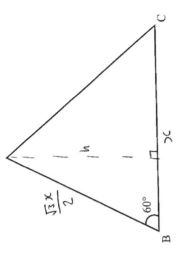

	W	W	W	T	T
W		•	•	⫽	⫽
W	•		•	⫽	⫽
W	•	•		⫽	⫽
T	⫽	⫽	⫽		⫽⫽
T	⫽	⫽	⫽	⫽⫽	

First pick

Total possibilities:

$5 \times 5 - 5 = 20$

$$\frac{6}{20} = \frac{3}{10} \qquad \frac{3}{10} \times 150 = 45$$

The table is a simple way of showing the different possibilities:

- The contents of the bag are shown along each side.
- The diagonal is shaded, because having picked one item from the bag, **you cannot take the same thing out as your second pick**: it is in your hand already.
- A dot is placed in each box which represents the result we want (two sweets).

The table shows us that there are 20 possibilities (leaving out the shaded squares), and 6 of these give two sweets.

Each time you conduct the experiment, there is a $\frac{6}{20}$ or $\frac{3}{10}$ chance of getting two sweets.

- Multiply this by 150, and you get the answer: 45.

Marking: 2 marks for finding the probability. 2 marks for estimating the number of results. Deduct 1 mark for a minor error in either part. **[4 marks]**

---

10   Here is the triangle, labelled with the information we might need:

```
          A
         /|\
        / | \
  √3x  /  |h \  √3x
   2  /   |   \   2
     /    |    \
    /_60°_|___□_\
   B      x      C
```

For convenience (and because 'BC' looks confusingly like 'B × C'), BC has been labelled x

I will offer two methods for solving this. The simplest and best method comes second – it should demonstrate that you can save time if you remember the rules of trigonometry!

The first method uses the trigonometric identities for right-angled triangles (usually remembered as **SOH – CAH – TOA**. See **Paper 3, Question 12(b)**).

Method 1 (slower)

Ⓐ $\sin 60° = \dfrac{h}{\left(\dfrac{\sqrt{3}x}{2}\right)}$ ∴ $\sin 60° = \dfrac{2h}{\sqrt{3}x}$ ∴ $h = \dfrac{\sqrt{3}x \sin 60°}{2}$

Ⓑ $\sin 60° = \dfrac{\sqrt{3}}{2}$ ∴ $h = \dfrac{\sqrt{3}x}{2} \times \dfrac{\sqrt{3}}{2} = \dfrac{3x}{4}$

Ⓒ Area: $120 = \dfrac{hx}{2} = \dfrac{3x}{4} \times \dfrac{x}{2} = \dfrac{3x^2}{8}$

∴ $x^2 = \dfrac{120 \times 8}{3} = 320$

Ⓓ ∴ $x = \sqrt{320} = \sqrt{4 \times 80} = \sqrt{4 \times 4 \times 20} = 4\sqrt{20}$

$= 4\sqrt{4 \times 5} = \underline{8\sqrt{5} \text{ cm}}$

This method is based on the formula $Area = \frac{Base \times Height}{2}$

To use this formula, we need to know the perpendicular height of the triangle, labelled h in the diagram above.

A: Using **SOH** ($\sin\theta = \frac{Opposite}{Hypotenuse}$), we can find an expression for h in terms of x …

B: … and substituting $\sin 60° = \frac{\sqrt{3}}{2}$ (see **Paper 3, Question 12(a)**), we find the equation $h = \frac{3x}{4}$

C: Because the area is 120cm² (from the question), $120 = \frac{1}{2}xh$

h is $\frac{3x}{4}$, so $120 = \frac{1}{2}x\left(\frac{3x}{2}\right)$

Simplifying, $x^2 = 320$

D: $\sqrt{320}$ simplifies to give $8\sqrt{5}$ (see [for example] **Paper 1, Question 10(a)(i)**).

- Don't forget the units (cm)!

Method 2 (faster)

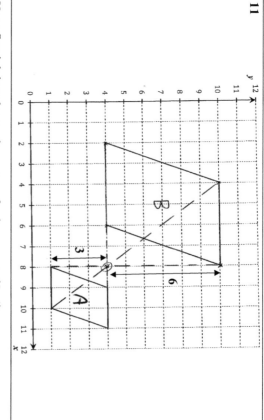

$Area = \frac{1}{2}ab\sin C$

$120 = \frac{1}{2} \times \frac{\sqrt{3}x}{2} \times x \sin 60°$ ⓐ

$\sin 60° = \frac{1}{2} \times \frac{\sqrt{3}}{2}$ ⓑ

$\therefore \sin 60° = \frac{\sqrt{3}}{2}$

$\therefore 120 = \frac{\sqrt{3}}{4}x^2 \times \frac{\sqrt{3}}{2} = \frac{3x^2}{8}$ ⓒ

$\therefore x^2 = \frac{8 \times 120}{3} = 320$

[Then use **Step D from Method 1**]

The formula $\mathbf{Area = \frac{1}{2}ab\sin C}$ (where C is an interior angle of a triangle and a and b are the sides adjacent to it) is very useful, because *it applies just as well when a triangle is not right-angled.*

A/B: Enter the values from the question into the formula, and apply your knowledge that $\sin 60° = \frac{\sqrt{3}}{2}$.

C: Find x^2

D: As in **Method 1**.

Marking: 4 marks for finding x^2. 2 marks for expressing x in surd form. Deduct 1 mark for each minor error. Up to 2 marks for reasonable attempt to find x^2 using one of the above methods, but with large errors. **[6 marks]**

11

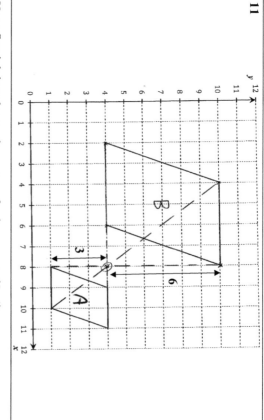

Your first job is to locate the centre of enlargement, $(8, 4)$.

Here we are dealing with a **negative** scale factor (-2), so you measure from each vertex (corner) of the original shape to the centre of enlargement, then *continue beyond it.*

If you are enlarging by a scale factor of 2 (or -2), you must go **twice as far again** as the distance between each of the vertices and the centre of enlargement (see the arrows in the example).

- For a scale factor of -3 you would go three times as far beyond, for a scale factor of $-\frac{5}{2}$ you would go two and a half times as far, and so on.

For a scale factor of -2 to use $(8, 4)$ as centre of enlargement. From remaining 2, subtract marks for errors. **[3 marks]**

Marking: 1 mark for clear attempt to use $(8, 4)$ as centre of enlargement. From remaining 2, subtract marks for errors. **[3 marks]**

This follows the principles outlined in **(i)**, but some algebra is needed to find the scale factor.

Once again, this uses the fact that the area of **A** is 6cm².

Marking: As for **(i)**. **[3 marks]**

12 The graph has been marked up for questions **(a)(i)** and **(b)**.

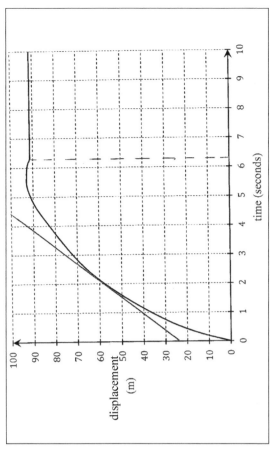

(a) (i)

6.3 seconds

Some people will be tempted to say that the ball strikes the ground at around 5.5 seconds, when it stops travelling forwards. However, you are told that it blows backwards: this is when it happens. What's more, there is no 'jolt' at this point – no sudden change: the jolt is later, at what looks like 6.3 seconds.

Any answer between 6.2 and 6.4 seconds would be acceptable here.

Marking: Any decimal or fraction, from 6.2 to 6.4 seconds. **[1 mark]**

(ii) *The ball instantly stops moving forwards or backwards.*

You need to say that it stops *immediately*.

(b) (i) $\left(\frac{2}{3}\right)^2 = \frac{4}{9}$ Area of A: $2 \times 3 = 6\ cm^2$

$$\frac{2\!\!\!/\,6}{} \times \frac{4}{9\!\!\!/\,3} = \frac{8}{3} = 2\frac{2}{3} = 2.6$$

$$= 2.67\ cm^2\ (2\ d.f.)$$

When you enlarge a shape by a scale factor, its area changes by **the square of the scale factor**:

- For example, if a shape has an area of 10cm² and is enlarged by a scale factor of 3, its new area will be 10×3^2, giving 90cm².
- This is because, if its length is increased by a scale factor of x and its height is also increased by a scale factor of x, its area must therefore be increased by $x \times x$, or x^2.

In the example above, the scale factor is $\frac{2}{3}$, so the area must change by $\left(\frac{2}{3}\right)^2$ or $\frac{4}{9}$ (in other words, its area decreases).

- Don't forget: the area of a parallelogram is **base × perpendicular height**.

Remember to give your answer as a decimal to 2 d.p.

Marking: 0 marks if does not understand 'square of scale factor' rule. 2 marks for minor error, 1 mark if rule understood but major errors. **[3 marks]**

(ii) When x is the scale factor:

$$(\text{Area of } A) \times x^2 = \left(10\tfrac{2}{3}\right)$$

$$6x^2 = \left(10\tfrac{2}{3}\right) = \frac{32}{3}$$

$$\therefore x^2 = \frac{32\ 16}{18\ 9} = \frac{16}{9}$$

$$\therefore x = \sqrt{\frac{16}{9}} = \frac{4}{3}$$

- To be strictly accurate, you should mention that it stops moving 'forwards or backwards', because *the graph does not tell you whether it rolls sideways*, but you should get the marks without this detail.

Marking: 1 mark for stopping; 1 mark for instantly/immediately etc. **[2 marks]**

(iii) *The ball falls increasingly steeply, then blows backwards slightly as it falls to earth.*

You are given in the question that the ball blows backwards. You need to identify that this is the point when it occurs.

You also need to mention that the ball falls more steeply, because this is also within the two seconds before the ball lands.

- Alternatively, you could say that the ball *falls straight* [albeit only instantaneously] then blows backwards.

Marking: 1 mark for falling more steeply/straight; 1 mark for backwards motion. **[2 marks]**

(b)

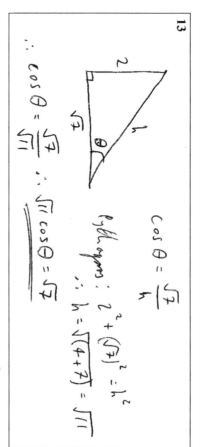

$$\text{Tangent at 2 seconds passes approximately}$$

$$\text{through } (1, 40) \text{ and } (4.5, 100)$$

$$\text{Gradient:} \quad \frac{100-40}{4.5-1} = \frac{60}{3.5} = \frac{120}{7} \approx 17 \, m/s$$

$$7 \overline{)120^{50}.0} \quad 17.1\ldots$$

To estimate the instantaneous velocity at 2 seconds, you need to draw a tangent to the graph at this point. (You must draw the tangent, because the question asks for it.)

- The instantaneous velocity is the **gradient** at this point, because velocity is $\frac{\text{change in distance}}{\text{time}}$.

You should strive to draw as accurate a tangent as possible. *Any answer between 14 and 20 m/s is likely to be acceptable*, so long as it is justified by your tangent and your calculations.

- Don't forget the units, m/s

Because you are asked to *estimate* the velocity, you should round appropriately. The unavoidable inaccuracy of a sketched tangent means that rounding to the nearest integer is reasonable.

Marking: 1 mark for attempting tangent at 2 seconds, even if poorly drawn. From 3 remaining, deduct marks for inaccuracy or errors (1 mark in this section if attempt to calculate gradient but otherwise incorrect). Maximum 3 marks total if answer not between 14 and 20 m/s. 3 marks for correct answer but wrong or missing units (ignore units in wrong answer). Maximum of 2 marks overall if no written working. Maximum of 3 if incomplete written working. **[4 marks]**

13

$$\cos\theta = \frac{\sqrt{7}}{h}$$

$$\text{Pythagoras:} \quad 2^2 + \left(\sqrt{7}\right)^2 = h^2$$

$$\therefore \sqrt{(4+7)} = h \quad \therefore h = \sqrt{(4+7)} = \sqrt{11}$$

$$\therefore \cos\theta = \frac{\sqrt{7}}{\sqrt{11}} \quad \therefore \sqrt{11}\cos\theta = \sqrt{7}$$

Because the question gives an equation for θ in the form $\tan\theta = \frac{a}{b}$ and specifies that θ is an acute angle, you have all the information you need to sketch a right-angled triangle.

Use the rule $\tan\theta = \frac{\text{opposite}}{\text{adjacent}}$ to determine which value goes where:

- We know that $\tan\theta = \frac{2}{\sqrt{7}}$, so 2 is the length of the side opposite the angle and $\sqrt{7}$ is adjacent to it.

The question asks you to find a result involving $\cos\theta$, which means that we need to apply the rule $\cos\theta = \frac{\text{adjacent}}{\text{hypotenuse}}$.

- First we must use Pythagoras' Theorem to find the hypotenuse: $\sqrt{11}$
- Entering this value and $\sqrt{7}$ in $\cos\theta = \frac{\text{adjacent}}{\text{hypotenuse}}$, we then rearrange to reach the required result.

Marking: 1 mark for attempt to sketch and label right-angled triangle or for attempt to use $\tan\theta = \dfrac{opposite}{adjacent}$. 2 marks if also an attempt to apply Pythagoras. 3 marks for a correct method with minor errors. **[4 marks]**

14 (a) (i)

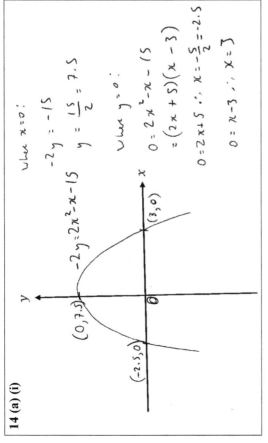

When $x = 0$:

$-2y = 2x^2 - x - 15$

$-2y = -15$

$y = \dfrac{15}{2} = 7.5$

When $y = 0$:

$0 = 2x^2 - x - 15$

$= (2x + 5)(x - 3)$

$0 = 2x + 5 \quad \therefore \quad x = -\dfrac{5}{2} = -2.5$

$0 = x - 3 \quad \therefore \quad x = 3$

The points where the graph crosses the axes are given where $x = 0$ (for the y-axis crossing) and where $y = 0$ (for the x-axis crossings).

In each case, you replace the relevant variables with 0, and solve.

Be sure to label the coordinates of the crossing points, and the graph itself.

- Because one of the y and x^2 terms is negative, this is an 'upside-down' quadratic: a hat, rather than a bowl.
- You can also think of a 'smiley face' for a positive quadratic (*it feels positive!*) and a 'sad face' for a negative quadratic (*it feels negative*).

Make your curve reasonably neat, so that the overall shape is correct for a quadratic and so that the maximum (turning) point is mid-way between the two x-axis crossing-points.

Marking: 1 mark for correct shape of graph but wrong crossing points. 2 marks for minor errors. 2 marks for correct crossings but graph upside down. Reward relevant working but wholly incorrect graph with 1 mark. **[3 marks]**

(ii)

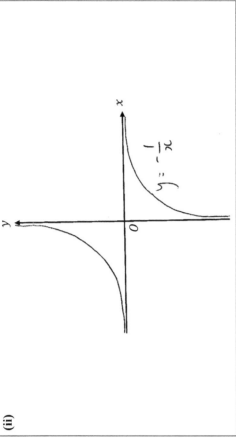

$y = -\dfrac{1}{x}$

You could sketch this graph by finding some values (e.g. where $x = 5$, $-\dfrac{1}{x} = -\dfrac{1}{5}$) to give you an idea of the shape.

However, you are expected at GCSE to recognise the shape of the graph $y = \dfrac{1}{x}$.

- The graph of $y = -\dfrac{1}{x}$ occupies *the other two quadrants of the graph.*

Bear in mind that this graph does not touch or cross the axes (x and y cannot equal 0), so it is important that your sketch is accurate in this respect.

Marking: 1 mark if sketches $y = \dfrac{1}{x}$ or if graph in only one quadrant, but broadly correct shape. 2 marks for minor errors e.g. touches (but does not cross) axes. Reward relevant working but wholly incorrect graph with 1 mark. **[3 marks]**

(iii)

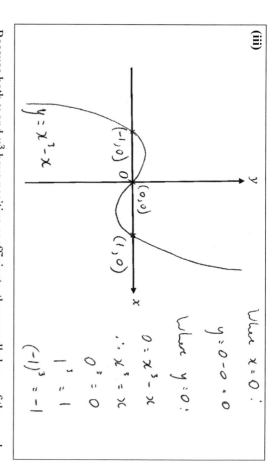

When $x = 0$:
$y = 0 - 0 = 0$

When $y = 0$:
$0 = x^3 - x$
$\therefore x^3 = x$
$0^3 = 0$
$1^3 = 1$
$(-1)^3 = -1$

$y = x^3 - x$

Because both y and x^3 have positive coefficients, the overall shape of the graph runs up from left to right.

- You could check this by testing a value of x (e.g. $x = 2$) after finding the axis intersects.

Finding the y-axis crossing, where $x = 0$, is simple.

To find the x-axis crossings, you need to make y equal 0:

- If $0 = x^3 - x$ then (by rearranging) $x^3 = x$
- This is true where $x = 0, 1$ or -1

You can also find these points by factorising:

$$0 = x^3 - x$$
$$0 = x(x^2 - 1)$$
$$0 = x(x + 1)(x - 1)$$

Marking: 1 mark for a plausible cubic graph (even if upside down) but wrong crossing points. 2 marks for minor errors. Reward relevant working but wholly incorrect graph with 1 mark. 2 marks if correct crossing points but graph upside down. **[3 marks]**

(b)

$$\underline{\underline{(1, -1)}} \quad \underline{\underline{(-1, 1)}}$$

If you are familiar with the graph of $y = \frac{1}{x}$ this answer may be obvious to you. This is why the question invites you simply to 'write down' the answer.

However, the answer also comes from thinking about the equation and graph of $y = -\frac{1}{x}$:

- As x becomes high or low, y moves further from the origin.
- As y becomes high or low, x moves further from the origin.

Therefore we need the values where there is *least difference between the magnitudes of x and y*.

Ideally, this will be where $|y| = |x|$. That is, where the *modulus* of y (the value of y if you ignore the positive or negative sign) equals the modulus of x, or as close to it as possible.

- Looking at $y = -\frac{1}{x}$, we can see that $y = 1$ where $x = -1$ and vice versa, giving $(1, -1)$ and $(-1, 1)$ as the points where the graph runs closest to the origin.

Marking: 1 mark for each. No f.t. marks from (a)(ii). **[2 marks]**

---

15 (a) Method 1

$$0.06\dot{4}\dot{4} = 0.06\dot{4}$$

Let $x = 0.06\dot{4}$

$100x = 6.\dot{4}$

$1000x = 64.\dot{4}$

$1000x - 100x = 64.\dot{4} - 6.\dot{4}$

$\therefore 900x = 58$

$x = \dfrac{58}{900} = \dfrac{29}{450}$

For another example and a fuller explanation, see **Paper 4, Question 13(c)**.

Firstly, it will make life a lot easier if you realise that $0.06\overline{44}$ can be written more simply as $0.06\dot{4}$

Let the decimal $0.06\dot{4}$ be called 'x'.

- Now we need two multiples of x: one which has the decimal point immediately before the recurring digits, and one which has the decimal point immediately after them.

Subtract these multiples to find an equation for x with no recurring element.

Rearrange and cancel to find the value of x ($0.06\dot{4}$ or $0.06\overline{44}$) as a fraction.

If you did not simplify the original decimal, you might have found the correct answer like this:

Method 2   Let $x = 0.06\overline{44}$ $100x = 6.\overline{44}$

$10000x = 644.\overline{44}$

$\therefore 10000x - 100x = 644.\overline{44} - 6.\overline{44}$

$9900x = 638$

$x = \dfrac{638}{9900} = \dfrac{319}{4950} = \dfrac{29}{450}$

Marking: 2 marks if minor errors. 1 mark for overall understanding of method but major or multiple errors. **[3 marks]**

(b) Method 1

$$333\,\overline{)\,40.000000} = 0.120120\ldots$$

or

$$0.1\dot{2}\dot{0}$$

Method 2

$$333 = 9 \times 37$$

(factor tree: $333 \to 3,\ 111 \to 3,\ 37$)

$$\therefore \frac{40}{333} = 40 \div 37 \div 9$$

$$37\,\overline{)\,40.000\ldots} = 1.081081\ldots$$

$$9\,\overline{)\,1.081081\ldots} = 0.1\dot{2}\dot{0}$$

Method 2 involves three steps, but each one is simpler than **Method 1**.

- **Factorise 333** in order to break the division into stages.
- Divide by one factor.
- Divide your result by the other factor.

Marking: As for (a). **[3 marks]**

16 (a)

(A) $\left(5(x^2+y^2) = 125 \right.$

(B) $\left. 3y = 15-x \quad \therefore \quad x = 15-3y \right)$

Substituting: $5([15-3y]^2 + y^2) = 125$

(C) $5(225 - 90y + 9y^2 + y^2) = 125$

$5(10y^2 - 90y + 225) = 125$

$10y^2 - 90y + 225 = 25$

$10y^2 - 90y + 200 = 0$

(D) $y^2 - 9y + 20 = 0$

$(y-5)(y-4) = 0$

$y-5 = 0 \quad \therefore \quad y = 5$

$y-4 = 0 \quad \therefore \quad y = 4$

(E) because $3y = (15-x)$

When $y=5$
$15 = 15-x$
$\therefore x = 0$

When $y = 4$
$12 = 15 - x$
$-3 = -x$
$x = 3$

(F) $\underline{\underline{(0, 5)}}$ and $\underline{\underline{(3, 4)}}$

To find the points where graphs intersect (whether or not they are straight lines), you need to solve their equations simultaneously.

Because one of our equations contains squared values and the other does not, we *cannot solve by elimination (subtraction or addition).*

- Instead, we must use substitution.

A: In order to substitute the second equation into the first, we must rearrange it in the form $x = \cdots$ or $y = \cdots$

- At this point you could also rewrite the first equation as $x^2 + y^2 = 25$. The example does not do this at step **C**.

B: Substitute the rearranged second equation (in the example, $x = 15 - 3y$) into the first.

C: Simplify.

D: Rearrange into the form $ay^2 + by + c = 0$ and simplify further.
Solve to find the two values of y.

E: Use either of the original equations to find the x value which belongs with each of the y values from step **D**.

F: State your answer as two coordinate pairs.

Marking: 4 marks if a minor error or two. 3 marks if a good overall approach, spoilt by several minor errors or a larger one. 2 marks if good overall approach and some correct working, but much wrong. 1 mark for some attempt to solve using substitution. **[5 marks]**

(b) $5(x^2 + y^2) = 125$ *is a circle, so a straight line can only cross it in 2 places.*

or

A quadratic equation (as formed after combining the equations in part (a)) has a maximum of 2 solutions.

The intention behind this question is that you identify the first equation as a circle, but the second option above would also be correct.

The second option would probably be acceptable without the clarification in brackets: this is only a one-mark question. Nonetheless, it does make the answer more persuasive.

Marking: Any clear and relevant answer. **[1 mark]**

17

(A) $p = \dfrac{k}{q}$

(B) when $q = 6$ and $p = 10$: $10 = \dfrac{k}{6}$ ∴ $k = 60$

(C) $p = \dfrac{60}{q}$

(D) when $q = 9$: $p = \dfrac{60}{9} = \dfrac{20}{3}$ **or** $6.\dot{6}$

There are two steps needed to answer this question:

- Find an equation relating p and q.
- Use this equation to find the value of p when q is 9.

A: If p is **inversely proportional** to q, then $\boldsymbol{p = \dfrac{k}{q}}$ where k is a number.

- You could also write this as $q = \dfrac{k}{p}$

B: Entering the given values of q and p (6 and 10), we can solve to find the value of k, which is 60.

C: This allows us to rewrite $p = \dfrac{k}{q}$ as $p = \dfrac{60}{q}$

D: Substituting $q = 9$ from the question, we find that $p = \dfrac{20}{3}$ or $6.\dot{6}$

Marking: 3 marks for finding equation for p and q; 1 mark for solving it correctly with $q = 9$ (allow f.t. mark if first part of answer produces incorrect equation). Deduct 1 or 2 marks for minor errors. Award at least 1 mark for answers which state $p = \dfrac{k}{q}$ or an equivalent. **[4 marks]**

END OF PAPER 5 SOLUTIONS   **TOTAL 100 MARKS**

Paper 6 (100 marks)

If you wish to complete this paper in timed conditions, allow 1hr 30mins.

1 Frank records the amount of TV he watches each day and his mean mark for homework tasks completed that day.

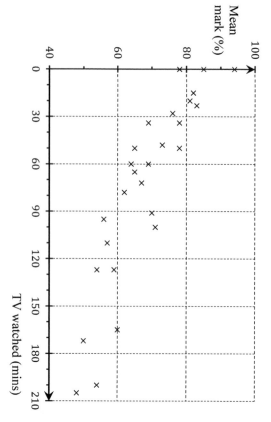

(a) Draw a line of best fit.

[2]

(b) What type of correlation is shown?

.... [1]

(c) Frank wants to use the data to decide how much TV he should allow himself to watch each day. He wants to achieve a mean mark above 60% for each day's homework in the future.

<u>Using your line of best fit</u>, how many minutes of TV would you advise Frank to permit himself each day?

Give your answer <u>as a range</u>, using appropriate inequality symbols.

.... [3]

2 John says that two values of x for which $x^2 - x = 20$ are -5 and -4.

Is he correct about one or both of these values, or is he incorrect?

You must show your working.

.... [3]

3 (a) Rationalise the denominator and simplify:

$$\frac{3\sqrt{8}}{\sqrt{6}}$$

.... [3]

5   Researchers from Harvard University surveyed 500 people to find out how many of six different kinds of fruit they ate in a week.

Their results are summarised in the following box plots.

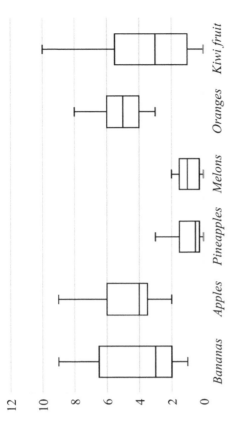

Bananas   *Apples*   *Pineapples*   *Melons*   *Oranges*   *Kiwi fruit*

(a)   What was the interquartile range of the number of apples eaten?

You must show your calculations.

.... **[2]**

(b)   For which fruit was the number eaten per week must consistent?
Explain your answer.

.... **[2]**

(b)   Write $0.3\overline{23}$ as a fraction in its lowest terms.

.... **[3]**

4   Find the area of the following triangle.

Not drawn accurately

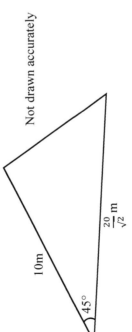

10m

$\frac{20}{\sqrt{2}}$ m

45°

.... **[4]**

(c)   Write down two similarities between the distributions of the
numbers of kiwi fruits and bananas eaten.

....

(d)   Which fruit was most popular?
Give a reason for your answer.

.... [2]

.... [2]

6   **A**, **B** and **C** are points on the circumference of a circle.

O is the centre of the circle.

The line AD is a tangent to the circle at **A**.

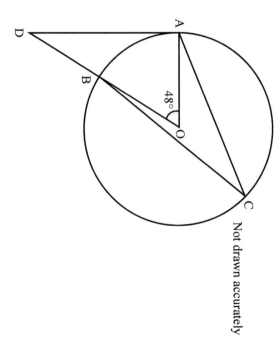

Not drawn accurately

(a)   What is the size of angle ADO?
Give a reason for your answer.

.... [2]

(b) What is the size of angle ACB?

Give a reason for your answer.

.... [2]

7 A triangle has vertices $(1 , 5)$, $(1 , 9)$ and $(7 , 5)$ on a centimetre grid.

(a) The triangle is translated by the vector $\begin{pmatrix} 6 \\ 0 \end{pmatrix}$

How many invariant points are on the perimeter of the triangle?

.... [1]

(b) The triangle is enlarged by a scale factor, creating a new triangle with an area of 108cm².

What is the scale factor of the enlargement?

.... [4]

Show that the line $-11y - 3 = 3x$ is <u>not</u> perpendicular to the line $2y = 11x - 46$

[3]

8

9 Miriam works out that when a cat comes to her door in the evening, there is a probability of 0.4 that it is her cat, Maisie.

If Maisie comes to the door, Miriam will let her in for the night. Assume that in all other ways the events are independent.

Four cats come to Miriam's door on Sunday evening.

What is the probability that Maisie comes home that evening?

.... [4]

10 This diagram shows three straight lines.

Where x is a constant:

Angle $a = (8x - 10)°$

Angle $b = (6x - 20)°$

Angle $c = (5x + 35)°$

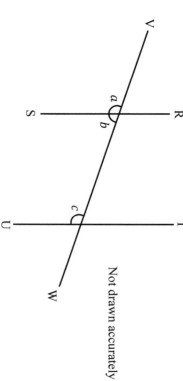

Not drawn accurately

Show that RS is parallel to TU.

_____

[4]

11 Two rectangular sports pitches have side lengths which are integers when measured in metres.

The longer side of each pitch is three times the length of the shorter side.

The difference between the areas of the two pitches is 168m².

Neither pitch is longer than 40m.

Find the area of the smaller pitch.

.... [5]

12 The masses of two sheep, Buttercup and Meersham, are in the ratio **B** : **M** on the 22nd of February.

When Buttercup gains 10kg and Meersham loses 10kg, the ratio becomes 1 : 2.

When both sheep lose 15kg (compared to their masses on the 22nd of February) the ratio becomes 1 : 3.

Express the ratio **B** : **M** in its lowest terms.

.... **[5]**

---

13 $f(x) = c - 3x$

$g(x) = \frac{c}{2}x - 4$

$fg(x) = d - 9x$

c and d are constants.

Work out the values of c and d.

.... **[6]**

14   Miss Pongle sets her class the following problem:

A sphere, A, has a volume of 343cm³.

A second sphere, B, has a radius three times as long as the radius of sphere A.

What is the volume of sphere B?

To solve this problem, Anton uses the following method:

- Find the square root of 343.
- Multiply the answer by 27.
- Square this number.

(a)   There is one mistake (an incorrect word or number) in each of Anton's bullet points. Rewrite them correctly, <u>changing nothing except the single mistake in each line</u>.

.... [3]

(b)   Solve the problem using a <u>different method</u>, which does **not** involve finding a root of 343.

.... [3]

---

15   The circle $x^2 + y^2 = 20$ has centre O.

Point **T** is on the circle's circumference and has a y coordinate of 2.

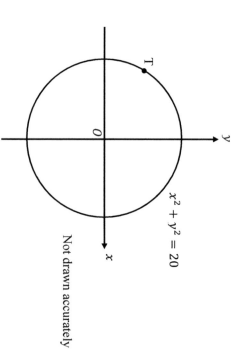

Not drawn accurately

Show that the tangent at **T** passes through the point $(41 , 92)$.

.... [6]

16 To build a house in 40 days, Erika employs 20 people, each working for 6 hours per day.

Matthew says that if Erika employs more people, each working for 8 hours per day, the job can be completed in 30 days.

(a) If Erika follows Matthew's advice of increasing working time to 8 hours per day, is it correct that more workers will be needed in order to finish in 30 days?

Assume that every person always works at the same rate.

You must show your working.

.... **[4]**

(b) How is the assumption that every person always works at the same rate likely to have affected your answer to part (a)?

Explain your answer.

.... **[3]**

---

17 This diagram shows a triangle and a sector of a circle with radius r.

The sector's radius is $\frac{1}{3}$ of the length of side a and $\frac{2}{3}$ of the length of side b.

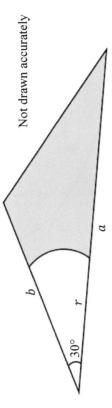

Not drawn accurately

Express the shaded area as a fraction of the area of the whole triangle, simplifying your answer as far as possible.

Use the approximate value $\pi = 3$.

.... **[6]**

---

18 This graph shows the velocity of a tortoise over a period of two minutes.

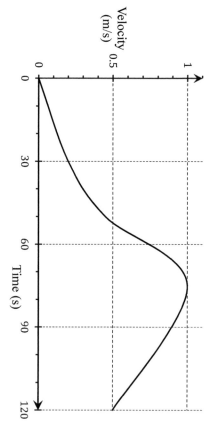

Velocity
(m/s)

(a) What is the tortoise's average acceleration over the first 75 seconds?

.... [2]

(b) Radhika says that the tortoise's instantaneous acceleration at 20 seconds is roughly the same as its average acceleration over the whole two minutes.

Do you agree?

You must show your working.

.... [4]

19 This solid has a uniform cross-section, formed by a right-angled isosceles triangle and a semi-circle.

x is a length in cm.

Not drawn accurately

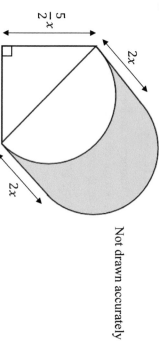

Show that the volume of the solid can be expressed as $\frac{25}{4}x^3\left(1+\frac{\pi}{2}\right)$ cm³.

[6]

END

TOTAL FOR PAPER 6 IS 100 MARKS

Paper 6 – Solutions

1 (a)

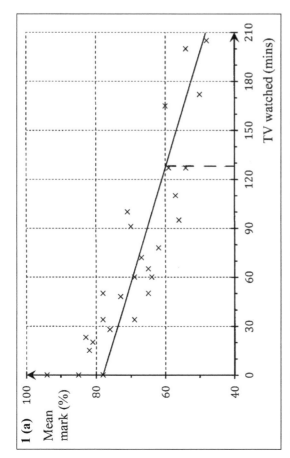

Mean mark (%)

TV watched (mins)

Your line of best fit should have a similar number of data points above and below it, and should follow the overall trend of the data.

It must touch the vertical axis line, because the data points reach this far.

Marking: 1 mark if plausibly follows the trend of the data, but clearly inaccurate; or if similar number of points above and below, but does not follow the direction of the data. **[2 marks]**

(b) *Negative correlation*

Negative correlation can be remembered as 'While one variable increases, the other *decreases*'. (**Positive correlation** is when both variables increase together.)

Marking: 'Negative' is acceptable without the word 'correlation'. **[1 mark]**

(c)

$$0 \leq \text{Amount of TV} < 128 \text{ mins}$$

or

$$0 \leq \text{Amount of TV} \leq 128 \text{ mins}$$

Answers should be based on the line of best fit from **(a)**. 130 minutes (instead of 128) would be fine: we are dealing with an approximation anyway.

For the same reason, it does not matter whether the second inequality is < or ≤.

However, **the first inequality must be** ≤, because Frank is allowed to watch no TV!

- You must include 0, because you are asked for a **range.**

Marking: 1 mark for the 0; 1 mark for 128/130 (or appropriate number based on student's best fit line); 1 mark for 0 ≤ ... Subtract a mark if units are missing. Do not subtract a mark if 'Amount of TV' is written as 'x' or similar. **[3 marks]**

---

2   **Method 1**

$$(-5)^2 - (-5) = 25 + 5 = 30 \quad \text{not} -5$$

$$(-4)^2 - (-4) = 16 + 4 = 20 \quad -4 \checkmark$$

−4 is correct but −5 is incorrect

or

He is correct about one value

You could also say that he is 'incorrect about one value'.

This method simply involves inserting each of the given values into $x^2 - x$ and seeing whether this gives a result of 20.

Method 2

$$x^1 - x = 20$$
$$\therefore x^2 - x - 20 = 0 \qquad x + 4 = 0$$
$$\qquad\qquad\qquad x = -4$$
$$(x+4)(x-5) = 0 \qquad x - 5 = 0$$
$$\qquad\qquad\qquad x = 5$$

<u>He is correct about one value</u>

This method involves solving the equation, and seeing whether the solutions match John's values.

Marking: 1 mark for correctly finding each value; 1 mark overall if some sign of correct method but mistakes in both calculations. **[3 marks]**

3 (a)

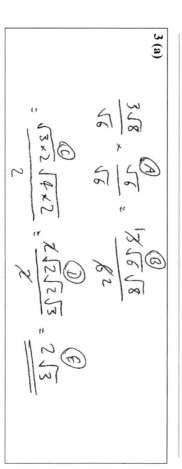

$$\frac{3\sqrt{8}}{\sqrt{6}} \times \overset{Ⓐ}{\frac{\sqrt{6}}{\sqrt{6}}} = \frac{\overset{Ⓑ}{3\sqrt{6}\sqrt{8}}}{6}$$

$$= \frac{\overset{Ⓒ}{\sqrt{3\times2}\,\sqrt{4\times2}}}{2} = \frac{\overset{Ⓓ}{2\sqrt{2}\sqrt{2}\sqrt{3}}}{2} = \overset{Ⓔ}{2\sqrt{3}}$$

A: Multiply by $\frac{\sqrt{6}}{\sqrt{6}}$ (which equals 1) to **rationalise the denominator** (see **Paper 1, Question 10(a)(i)**).

B: Simplify.

C: Factorize into square roots of square numbers where possible ($\sqrt{4}$) and square roots of primes in all other cases.

D/E: Simplify.

It would also be acceptable to simplify $\frac{3\sqrt{8}}{\sqrt{6}}$ before rationalising the denominator, although the question encourages the opposite approach.

Marking: 1 mark for correct method for rationalising denominator (even if mistakes). 1 mark for decent attempt to simplify. **[3 marks]**

(b)

$$\text{let } x = 0.3\overline{23} \qquad\qquad 1000x - 10x = 323.2\overline{3} - 3.2\overline{3}$$
$$\therefore 10x = 3.2\overline{3} \qquad\qquad \therefore 990x = 320$$
$$1000x = 323.2\overline{3} \qquad\qquad\qquad x = \frac{320}{990} = \frac{32}{99}$$

$$\underline{\underline{x = \frac{32}{99}}}$$

For a full explanation of this method, see **Paper 4, Question 13(c)** or **Paper 5, Question 15(a)**.

Marking: 2 marks if minor errors. 1 mark if some understanding. **[3 marks]**

4

$$Area = \frac{1}{2}bc\sin A = \frac{1}{2} \times 10 \times 20\,\sin45°$$
$$= 100\,\sin45° = \frac{100}{\sqrt{2}} = \frac{100}{\sqrt{2}} \times \frac{\sqrt{2}}{2} = \underline{\underline{50\,m^2}}$$

To solve this, you need to know:

- The sine formula for the area of a triangle, $Area = \frac{1}{2}bc\sin A$
- That $\sin45° = \frac{\sqrt{2}}{2}$ (see **Paper 3, Question 12(a)**)

Marking: 3 marks if 1 minor error. 2 marks for several minor errors. 1 mark if a major error. Max mark of 2 if it doesn't know that $\sin45° = \frac{\sqrt{2}}{2}$. **[4 marks]**

5 (a)

$$6 - 3.5 = 2.5$$

The upper and lower quartiles of a box plot are *the ends of the box*.

The **interquartile range** is *the difference between the upper and lower quartiles* ($Q_3 - Q_1$).

Marking: 1 mark for fully correct calculations based on wrong values or for calculation error based on correct values. Permit answers based on a value between 3.25 and 3.75 (e.g. 6 − 3.75 = 2.25). **[2 marks]**

(b) *Melons, because the range is the smallest and the interquartile range is the joint smallest.*

You could make **either one** of the points in the example, but both are relevant so a full answer is preferable.

The logic here is that *data is most consistent where there is least variation*: range and interquartile range both indicate how varied the data is.

Marking: 1 mark if Melons but explanation weak or missing. **[2 marks]**

(c) *They have the same interquartile range and the same median.*

The **median** is shown by the line within each box.

Marking: 1 mark for each. **[2 marks]**

(d) *Oranges, because the median consumption was highest.*

Averages/measures of central tendency give us an indication of the character of a group. Remember that each kind of average (mean, median, mode) has different strengths and weaknesses as a description of the overall data.

Marking: 1 mark if Oranges but explanation weak or absent. **[2 marks]**

---

6 (a) Angle between a tangent and a radius is $90°$.

$$\therefore \ D\hat{A}O = 90°$$

$$(180 - (90 + 48) = (180 - 138) = 42°$$

A radius forms a right-angle with the tangent which meets the circumference at the same point — which is a complicated way of explaining something quite obvious!

You need to state a version of this fact as your explanation. Simply writing that there are 180° in a triangle would not be enough to get the second mark: you need to explain where the missing angle (90°) comes from.

Marking: 1 mark for correct answer. 1 answer for reasonably clear explanation of right-angle/tangent rule. **[2 marks]**

(b) Angle subtended at circumference is half angle at centre.

$$\therefore \ A\hat{C}B = \frac{A\hat{O}B}{2} = \frac{48}{2} = 24°$$

More fully, the angle subtended by two lines at the circumference is half the angle subtended at the centre by lines drawn from the same two points.

For an explanation of this principle, see **Paper 4, Question 1**.

Marking: 1 mark for correct answer. 1 answer for clear explanation of rule. Word 'subtended' not required. **[2 marks]**

7 (a)

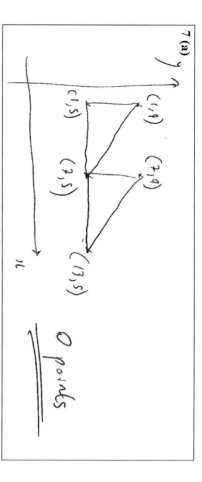

An **invariant point** is a point which does not vary – which does not change.

As the sketch shows, the triangle has a vertex at (7 , 5) before and after the translation … but *different vertices* occupy this point, so *it is not invariant*.

You do not need to show any working, because the question is only worth one mark and you may already know that **a translation permits no invariant points.**

Marking: Correct answer only. **[1 marks]**

(b)

(A) Old area: $\frac{1}{2} \times 6 \times 4 = 12 \text{ cm}^2$

(B) $\frac{108}{12} = 9$ (C) $\sqrt{9} = 3$

Remember: *the area of a shape increases by **the square of the scale factor.***

A: You need to recognise that the original coordinates form a right-angled triangle. Its area is therefore given by $\frac{1}{2} \times base \times height$ (strictly speaking, *perpendicular* height).

B: The area is increased 9 times in the enlargement.

C: The scale factor must be the square root of the increase in area.

Marking: 3 marks if all steps understood but an error. 2 marks if one step not understood. 1 mark if some understanding. **[4 marks]**

8

(A) $-11y - 3 = 3x \quad \therefore -11y = 3x + 3 \quad \therefore y = -\frac{3}{11}x - \frac{3}{11}$

$2y = 11x - 46 \quad \therefore y = \frac{11}{2}x - 23$

Gradients are $-\frac{3}{11}$ and $\frac{11}{2}$

(B) Neg. recip. of $-\frac{3}{11}$ is $\frac{11}{3}$

(C) $\frac{11}{3} \neq \frac{11}{2}$ so the lines are not perpendicular.

When you have to show that something **is not the case**, you should start by considering how you would *prove the opposite*:

• If two lines are perpendicular, their gradients are **negative reciprocals** of each other: $\frac{a}{b}$ and $-\frac{b}{a}$.

Therefore you simply need to show that the gradients of these two lines are **not** negative reciprocals of each other.

A: When the equation of a line is written in the form $y = mx + c$, its gradient is m. Therefore the first job is to **rearrange both equations** into this form and **write down the two gradients**.

B: **Find the negative reciprocal** of one of the gradients.

C: Explain that this does not equal the other gradient.

A more 'mathematical' way of approaching this question would involve recognising that **gradients of perpendicular lines have a product of −1.**

• Having found the gradients:

$$\frac{-3}{11} \times \frac{11}{2} = -\frac{3}{2}$$

$-\frac{3}{2} \neq -1$, $\therefore$ lines are not perpendicular

Marking: 2 marks if well understood but proof inadequate. 2 marks if well-constructed proof but an error or two. 1 mark if some understanding (e.g. some attempt to find neg. recip. or product of gradients). **[3 marks]**

9   Method 1

$$1 - 0.6^4 = 1 - 0.1296$$
$$= 0.8704$$

$$6^4 = 36^2$$

$$\begin{array}{r} 36 \\ \times\ 36 \\ \hline 216 \\ 1080 \\ \hline 1296 \end{array}$$

$$\begin{array}{r} 0.8889 \\ 0.1296 \\ \hline 0.8704 \end{array}$$

This is the simplest approach (the important working is at the top – the rest is just calculation).

- The probability that Maisie **does not come home** on any of the four occasions is $0.6 \times 0.6 \times 0.6 \times 0.6 = 0.1296$
- … so the probability that she **does** is the remainder: $1 - 0.1296 = 0.8704$

You could also calculate the likelihood that Maisie DOES come home on **each** occasion, then add your answers together:

Method 2 (1st time: 0.4

2nd time: $0.6 \times 0.4 = 0.24$

3rd time: $0.6 \times 0.6 \times 0.4 = 0.144$

4th time: $0.6 \times 0.6 \times 0.6 \times 0.4 = 0.0864$

$$\begin{array}{r} 0.4000 \\ +\ 0.2400 \\ +\ 0.1440 \\ +\ 0.0864 \\ \hline 0.8704 \end{array}$$

- On the first occasion that a cat comes to Miriam's door, there is a 0.4 chance that it is Maisie.
- The chance that the second cat is Maisie is 0.4 × *the probability that the **first cat was not** Maisie*

… and so on.

The disadvantages of this method are that it takes longer, and that the greater number of calculations increases the risk of error.

Marking: 3 marks if good method with a minor error or two. 2 marks if good understanding but more problems. 1 mark if some correct work. **[4 marks]**

10

RS is parallel to TU if $a = c$

$$a + b = 180° \quad \therefore (8x - 10) + (6x - 20) = 180$$
$$\therefore 14x - 30 = 180$$
$$\therefore 14x = 210 \quad \therefore x = \frac{210}{14} = \frac{30}{2} = 15$$

If $x = 15$:

$$a = 8x - 10 = 120 - 10 = 110° \quad \therefore a = c$$
$$c = 5x + 35 = 75 + 35 = 110° \quad \therefore \text{RS and TU are parallel}$$

It is helpful to begin by stating what you wish to prove: **that a and c are the same** (alternate angles).

- (You could also prove that RS and TU are parallel by showing that b and c add up to 180°: interior angles.)

Because a and b add up to 180°, you can **form an equation** from the expressions for these letters and **solve it to find x.**

Substituting $x = 15$ into the equations for a and c, you can now show that they are the same.

Marking: 3 marks if good work but not presented as a proof – lacks indication of what results *mean*. 3 marks for good proof attempt with minor errors. 1 or 2 marks for good elements in problematic answer. **[4 marks]**

11

This is a question which does not appear to give enough information: therefore the best starting point is to **clearly set out what you do know**, preferably with the help of some simple sketches.

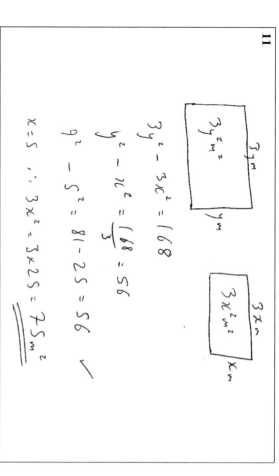

- If a shape has a side length y and another side which has length $3y$, the area of the shape is $3y^2$. (Likewise for x and $3x$.)
- The difference between the shapes' areas is 168m².

Combining and simplifying these facts, we reach the equation $y^2 - x^2 = 56$.

Because neither pitch is longer than 40m and x and y are whole numbers, the highest possible value of y is 13m ($3 \times 13 = 39$).

Therefore we need to find **integer values of y and x which are 13 or less**, such that $y^2 - x^2 = 56$. This can be achieved fairly easily through trial and error:

- For each value of y^2 you try, **subtract 56** and **ask yourself whether the result is a square number.**

Don't forget to complete your answer by finding **the area of the smaller pitch.**

Marking: 4 marks if minor error. 3 marks for multiple or larger errors in good overall approach. 1 or 2 marks for good things in a botched attempt. **[5 marks]**

12

$$2(B+10) = M-10 \quad \therefore M = 2B+20+10 = 2B+30$$
$$3(B-15) = M-15 \quad \therefore M = 3B-45+15 = 3B-30$$
$$(M = 2B+30) \quad (M = 3B-30) \quad \therefore 2B+30 = 3B-30$$
$$2B+60 = 3B \quad \therefore 60 = B$$
$$M = 2B+30 = 120+30 = 150$$
$$\therefore B:M = 60:150 = 2:5$$

A: If the new ratio is 1 : 2, then **twice** Buttercup's weight after her weight gain (**B** + 10) must equal Meersham's weight after weight loss (**M** − 10). Rearranging and simplifying, **M = 2B + 30.**

B: When the ratio is 1 : 3, **three times** Buttercup's weight after her weight loss (**B** − 15) must equal Meersham's weight after weight loss (**M** − 15). Rearranging and simplifying, **M = 3B − 30.**

C: Combining the two equations by **substitution**, we can create a single equation for **B.**

D: Solving, **B** = 60, so Buttercup's original weight was 60kg.

E: Taking one of the equations in **M** and **B**, we can find that Meersham's original weight was 150kg.

F: Writing these weights as a ratio and simplifying, we can find that the ratio **B : M** was 2 : 5.

Marking: As for **Question 11. [5 marks]**

Combining and solving, we find that $c = 6$

H: Because $c + 12 = d$ (from step **D**), $d = 18$

You don't need to use $x = 0$ and $x = 1$: any other two values would also work. However, these are the easiest.

The following method is not part of the GCSE syllabus, but it is simpler and therefore may be of interest. It uses the method of **comparing coefficients**.

$f(x) = c - 3x$ ①

$g(x) = \frac{c}{2}x - 4$ ②

$fg(x) = d - 9x$ ③

From ① and ②: $fg(x) = c - 3\left(\frac{c}{2}x - 4\right) = c - \frac{3c}{2}x + 12$ ④

Compare coefficients between ③ and ④ $\left(fg(x) \equiv fg(x)\right)$

$$d - 9x \equiv c + 12 - \frac{3c}{2}x$$

Coefficient of x must be the same:

$$-9 = -\frac{3c}{2} \implies \underline{\underline{c = 6}}$$

Constant terms must also be the same:

$$d = c + 12 = 6 + 12 = 18$$

$$\underline{\underline{d = 18}}$$

$\equiv$ is the symbol for an **identity**: meaning that the functions on each side of the sign are the same.

- $y = 2x$, for example, is **not** an identity: it is only true for some values of x and y.

I won't explain the method of comparing coefficients in detail as it is not a standard part of GCSE. However, some classes may cover it.

- In summary: For $ax + by \equiv cx + dy$ it must be true that $a = c$ and $b = d$, because there must be 'the same amount of x' and 'the same amount of

---

13

$f(x) = c - 3x$

Ⓐ $g(x) = \frac{c}{2}x - 4$ ∴ $fg(x) = c - 3\left(\frac{c}{2}x - 4\right)$

$\qquad = c - \frac{3}{2}cx + 12$

Ⓑ $fg(0) = c + 12$

Ⓕ from $fg(x) = d - 9x$ and $c + 12 = d$:

and $fg(x) = d - 9x$

Ⓒ $fg(0) = d$

Ⓓ ∴ $c + 12 = d$

Ⓔ $fg(1) = c - \frac{3}{2}c + 12$ Ⓖ $\left(fg(1) = d - 9x\right)$

$\qquad = -\frac{c}{2} + 12$ $\left(fg(1) = c + 3\right)$

$\qquad\qquad ∴ -\frac{c}{2} + 12 = c + 3 \quad ∴ 12 = \frac{3}{2}c + 3$

$\qquad\qquad ∴ 9 = \frac{3}{2}c \quad ∴ c = \frac{18}{3} = 6$

Ⓗ $c + 12 = d$ ∴ $d = 12 + 6 = 18$ $\underline{\underline{c = 6, \; d = 18}}$

A: Because we have expressions for $f(x)$ and $g(x)$, we can form an expression for $fg(x)$ by combining them: replace x in $c - 3x$ with $\frac{c}{2}x - 4$

We need to find c and d, so we want two equations without x.

B: If $fg(x) = c - \frac{3}{2}cx + 12$ (from step **A**) then $fg(0) = c + 12$

C: If $fg(x) = d - 9x$ (from the question) then $fg(0) = d$

D: Combining the equations from steps **B** and **C**, $c + 12 = d$

That's our first equation without x. But we need to know more, so **we need to form equations by using a different value of x.**

E: If $fg(x) = c - \frac{3}{2}cx + 12$ then $fg(1) = -\frac{c}{2} + 12$

F: If $fg(x) = d - 9x$ and $c + 12 = d$ then $fg(1) = c + 3$

G: We now have two equations giving $fg(1)$ in terms of c.

y' on each side of the equation if the functions $ax + by$ and $cx + dy$ are to be equivalent.

Marking: This is difficult, so be generous towards good ideas in a confused answer: up to 3 marks in this instance. 4 or 5 marks for major/minor errors in a largely well-constructed method. **[6 marks]**

14 (a)

- *Find the **cube** root of 343.*
- *Multiply the answer by 3.*
- ***Cube** this number.*

- Anton's first mistake is probably self-explanatory: to convert a **volume** into a **length**, we must cube root it.

(Be aware that the length obtained here *is not the radius*: it is another length which is *in proportion to the radius*. You do not need to worry about this.)

- Having found this length, we need to increase it by the ratio of radiuses (because these are also a length, and all lengths must change in the same proportion), which is 1 : 3.

- We now need to **convert this length into a new volume** by cubing it.

Marking: 1 mark for each part. **[3 marks]**

(b)

$$3^3 = 27$$

$$\begin{array}{r} 343 \\ \times\ 27 \\ \hline 2401 \\ 6860 \\ \hline 9261 \end{array}$$

$$9261\, cm^3$$

Volumes increase by **the ratio of lengths, cubed.**

- If the radius increases **3 times**, the volume must increase **27 times**.

Marking: 0 marks if uses method involving roots. 1 mark if a plausible attempt with problems. 2 marks if a minor error. **[3 marks]**

15

$$x^2 + y^2 = 20$$

$x^2 + y^2 = 20$

(A) $\therefore\ x^2 + 2^2 = 20$
$x^2 = 20 - 4 = 16$
$\therefore\ x = \pm 4$

(B) $\therefore\ T$ is $(-4, 2)$

(C) Gradient of line TO
$= \dfrac{0-2}{0-(-4)} = \dfrac{-2}{4} = -\dfrac{1}{2}$

(D) $\therefore$ Gradient of tangent $= \dfrac{2}{1} = 2$

(E) $y - y_1 = m(x - x_1)$ $\therefore$ $y - 2 = 2(x - (-4))$
$\therefore\ y = 2x + 8 + 2 = y = 2x + 10$

(F) where $x = 41$, $y = 2 \times 41 + 10 = 92$
$\therefore\ (41, 92)$ is a point on $y = 2x + 10$

Before starting work on a question like this, it is important to know where you are heading.

To show that the tangent passes through a certain point, you need to know its equation.

- Therefore we need to find the equation of the tangent at **T**.

A/B: Because we know the equation of the circle and the y coordinate of **T**, we can also **find its x coordinate.**

C: Find **the gradient of the radius**, TO.

D: The gradient of the tangent will be the **negative reciprocal** of the gradient of TO.

(b) A person who works for more hours in a day is likely to be more tired and work less effectively. Therefore the answer to (a) could have been 'yes', because more workers would be needed to finish in 30 days.

or

If the job is done in fewer days, less time is wasted in preparing each morning and packing up each evening. Therefore fewer than 20 people might be needed – which leaves the answer to (a) unchanged as 'no'.

Both answers are possible: the marks are for explaining your point of view clearly and for explaining how it might have affected the answer to **(a)**.

Marking: 2 marks for explanation, depending on clarity and thoroughness. 1 mark for clearly indicating effect on **(a)**. **[3 marks]**

17

Sector: Area $= \frac{30}{360}\pi r^2 = \frac{1}{12} \times 3r^2 = \frac{r^2}{4}$

Triangle: $\frac{1}{2}ab\sin C = \frac{1}{2}ab\sin 30° = \frac{ab}{4}$

Shaded area: $\frac{ab}{4} - \frac{r^2}{4} = \frac{1}{4}(ab - r^2)$

$$\frac{\frac{1}{4}(ab - r^2)}{\frac{1}{4}ab} = \frac{ab - r^2}{ab}$$

$a = 3r$ $b = \frac{3}{2}r$ (from question)

$$\frac{ab - r^2}{ab} = \frac{3r \times \frac{3}{2}r - r^2}{3r \times \frac{3}{2}r} = \frac{\frac{9}{2}r^2 - r^2}{\frac{9}{2}r^2} = \frac{\frac{7}{2}r^2}{\frac{9}{2}r^2} = \frac{7}{9} \text{ of total}$$

E: Using the formula $y - y_1 = m(x - x_1)$, with the gradient m from step **D** and the point $(-4, 2)$, we can find that the equation of the tangent at **T** is $y = 2x + 10$.

F: Confirm that the point $(41, 92)$ lies on the line $y = 2x + 10$ by substituting the x and y values.

Marking: 1 mark for finding point **T**. 2 marks for gradient of tangent. 2 marks for equation of tangent. 1 mark for checking point (41 , 92). Allow F.T. marks throughout. **[6 marks]**

16 (a)

Days	People	Hours
40	20	6
30	20	8

×3/4 (...) ×4/3

No: More workers are not needed.

A table is always helpful when dealing with proportional change.

- If the number of hours worked per day increases from 6 to 8, this is a $1\frac{1}{3}$ increase: 6 has been multiplied by $\frac{4}{3}$.

- Therefore the number of days needed can be divided by $\frac{4}{3}$... or multiplied by $\frac{3}{4}$ (*days worked* and *hours worked per day* are inversely proportional).

- This gives 30 days, which is the length of time suggested by Matthew – but without needing to increase the number of workers.

Remember to answer the question directly, by stating that Matthew is not correct.

- You could also solve this problem by working out that 20 people working for 6 hours per day for 40 days complete a total of 4800 hours' work (20 × 6 × 40 = 4800): 20 × 8 × 30 also equals 4800.

Marking: 1 mark for answer; 3 marks for working. F.T. for yes/no answer if based on wrong working. Working: 2 marks if minor error. 1 mark for problems but decent approach. **[4 marks]**

You need to know **the area of the shaded region** and **the area of the whole triangle**.

To find the shaded area you first need to know **the area of the unshaded sector**.

- The area of a sector with angle $\theta°$ is given by $\dfrac{\theta}{360}\pi r^2$, and we are told that for the purposes of this question $\pi = 3$.

  To find the area of the whole triangle, you need to use the formula $Area = \frac{1}{2}bc \sin A$ (see **Question 4**).

- $\sin 30° = \frac{1}{2}$ (see **Paper 3, Question 12(a)**)

  The area of the shaded region is given by *the area of the triangle –the area of the sector*.

  Then you need to **express the area of the shaded region as a fraction of the area of the whole triangle**, and simplify.

- You could also find the area of the unshaded sector as a fraction of the area of the triangle, then subtract this from 1.

  From the question we can see that $a = 3r$ and $b = \frac{3}{2}r$.

- **Substitute** these values and **simplify**.

You could also choose to substitute these values earlier in the solution.

Marking: 4 or 5 marks if minor errors in good method. 3 marks for a substantial amount of good work in a flawed answer. 1 or 2 marks for good elements in a poor answer. **[6 marks]**

18 (a)

Acceleration is $\dfrac{Change\ in\ Velocity}{Time}$.

The tortoise's velocity goes from 0 m/s to 1 m/s in the first 75 seconds (see graph in solution to **(b)** below), so the change in velocity is 1 m/s.

- Remember the units of acceleration: metres per second, per second, or m/s².

Marking: 1 mark for answer, 1 mark for units. **[2 marks]**

(b)

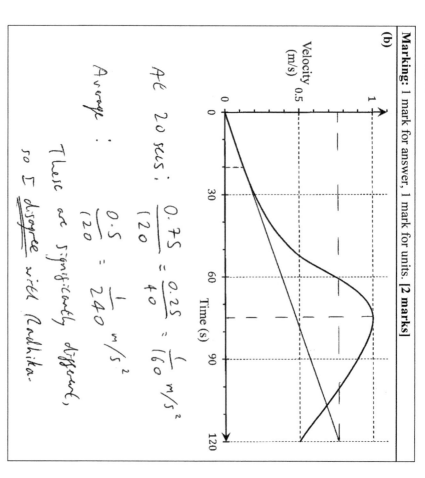

To estimate the tortoise's instantaneous acceleration at 20 seconds, you need to draw a tangent to the graph at this point and find its gradient (see **Paper 5, Question 12(b)** for a similar question).

- Any result between 0.0058 m/s² and 0.0071 m/s² is likely to be acceptable.

The average acceleration **over the whole distance** is *the overall change in velocity (i.e. the final velocity) divided by the total time.*

- This takes into account the tortoise's acceleration up to 75 seconds, and its deceleration after this point.

No reasonable estimate of the tortoise's instantaneous acceleration at 20 seconds could be said to support Radhika's statement: you are expected to **disagree** with her.

If 1 m/s sounds surprisingly quick, bear in mind that the fastest recorded speed for a tortoise on land is around 5mph (2.2 m/s)! They may be sluggish animals most of the time, but they can run when they need to.

Marking: 1 mark for reasonable tangent line. 1 mark each for instantaneous accel. and overall average. 1 mark for 'disagree' answer so long as supported by working. Up to 2 marks overall if decent approach but errors in several parts. [4 marks]

19

(A) Triangle: $\frac{1}{2} \times \frac{5}{2}x \times \frac{5}{2}x = \frac{25}{8}x^2$ cm²

(B) Hypotenuse: $a^2 + b^2 = h^2$ ∴ $\left(\frac{5}{2}x\right)^2 + \left(\frac{5}{2}x\right)^2 = h^2 = \frac{25}{2}x^2 = h^2$

∴ $h = \sqrt{\frac{25}{2}x^2} = \frac{5}{\sqrt{2}}x$ cm ∴ Radius is $\frac{5x}{2\sqrt{2}}$ cm

(C) Semi-circle: $\frac{1}{2}\pi r^2 = \frac{1}{2}\pi\left(\frac{5x}{2\sqrt{2}}\right)^2 = \frac{1}{2}\pi\frac{25x^2}{8} = \frac{25\pi x^2}{16}$ cm²

(D) Cross-section: $\frac{25}{8}x^2 + \frac{25}{16}\pi x^2 = \frac{25}{8}x^2\left(1 + \frac{\pi}{2}\right)$ cm²

$$\text{Volume} = 2x \times \frac{25}{8}x^2\left(1 + \frac{\pi}{2}\right) = \frac{25}{4}x^3\left(1 + \frac{\pi}{2}\right) \text{ cm}^3$$

B: To find the area of the semi-circle you need to know its radius.

- The radius of the semi-circle will be **half the length of the triangle's hypotenuse**. To find this, you need to use **Pythagoras' theorem** (already well covered in this pack).

C: The area of a semi-circle is **half the area of a circle with the same radius** (i.e. $\frac{1}{2}\pi r^2$).

D: **Add these together** to find the area of the cross section.

Factorise fully, because now we can see where we are heading.

E: **Multiply by the depth of the solid, $2x$**, to (hopefully!) produce the required expression.

This is the sort of question where it is very easy to make a tiny mistake which makes the answer incorrect – and very difficult to find such a mistake when checking back through your answer. It is important to approach such a question carefully, making sure that each calculation is correct, even if you are pressed for time.

- Knowing the destination should give you a helpful guide as you go along. If you seem to be heading in a different direction, stop and check your working.

Marking: 4 or 5 marks if minor errors in good method. 3 marks for a substantial amount of good work in a flawed answer. 1 or 2 marks for good elements in a poor answer. [6 marks]

END OF PAPER 6 SOLUTIONS   **TOTAL 100 MARKS**

This is a **prism**: a shape whose cross-section is repeated throughout.

- Its volume is **the area of its cross section, multiplied by its depth.**

To find the area of the cross section, it is necessary to deal with the triangle and the semi-circle separately.

A: The area of the triangle is $\frac{1}{2} \times$ *base* $\times$ *perpendicular height*. Because the triangle is right-angled and isosceles, the height and the base are the same length.